# Make Your Own Pictionary

### Preschool-Grade 1

## Craig Boultinghouse
### and
## Ellen Matlach Hassell

SNIFFEN COURT BOOKS/NEW YORK

# Pictionary Words

The following is an alphabetized list of the 150 words introduced in *Make Your Own Pictionary*.

| | | | | | | |
|---|---|---|---|---|---|---|
| airplane | boy | daddy | horn | one | scissors | towel |
| ant | broom | desk | horse | orange | seesaw | train |
| apple | brother | doctor | house | pan | shoes | tree |
| apron | brush | dog | ice | pants | sister | truck |
| baby | bus | doll | ice cream | paper | sled | T-shirt |
| ball | butterfly | door | jacket | paste | slide | tub |
| balloon | cake | dress | jar | pie | snake | turkey |
| banana | candy | drum | king | pig | snowman | turtle |
| barn | car | duck | kite | pillow | soap | two |
| basket | carrot | elephant | kitten | pool | socks | umbrella |
| bat | cat | fish | ladder | present | spider | valentine |
| bear | chair | five | lamp | pumpkin | spoon | wagon |
| bed | chicken | flag | leaf | puppy | squirrel | window |
| bicycle | clock | flower | lion | purple | sun | witch |
| bird | clown | fork | milk | queen | sweater | x-ray |
| blanket | coat | four | mitten | rabbit | swing | yellow |
| blue | comb | frog | mommy | radio | table | zebra |
| boat | cookies | girl | monkey | rainbow | teacher | zoo |
| book | corn | goat | moon | rake | telephone | |
| boots | cow | green | nest | red | television | |
| bottle | crayon | hat | numbers | rug | three | |
| bowl | cup | heart | nurse | school | tiger | |

**Cover Artist:**
Maxie Chambliss

**Artists:**
Maxie Chambliss
Ellen Matlach Hassell
Manuel Rivera

Special thanks to Sarah Armstrong and Morgan Sweet

ISBN 0-930790-09-X          SC-1008

# Table of Contents

# To The Teacher

## Introduction

An early interest in words is one of the most reliable predictors of success in learning to read. Even as toddlers, children gain a sense of pride in being able to name familiar objects in baby books. Preschoolers delight in being able to spot a familiar word in a magazine or on a billboard.

*Make Your Own Pictionary* is designed to capitalize on this natural curiosity to help your students become familiar with 150 of the most common nouns in beginning reading programs. By the time your students have completed this book, they will have compiled their own picture dictionary containing these 150 words plus any other words they want to add on their own.

### Skills
The activities in *Make Your Own Pictionary* develop:
- oral language
- letter recognition
- consonant sound/symbol association
- beginning dictionary skills
- beginning sight vocabulary
- color recognition

### Grade Level
- Preschool
- Kindergarten
- First Grade

At each level, students can benefit from the activities in *Make Your Own Pictionary*. For preschool children, the book provides an introduction to language without requiring mastery of the vocabulary or the alphabet.

For kindergarten students, creative activities in *Make Your Own Pictionary* provide opportunities to reinforce and supplement the basic kindergarten language curriculum leading to mastery of the skills outlined above.

For first grade students, *Make Your Own Pictionary* will be a compatible supplement to their basic reading program, providing the extra practice often needed for beginning readers.

## Organization

*Make Your Own Pictionary* is divided into twenty-five units, each made up of ten student pages introduced with a page of teacher instruction. Each unit introduces six words and one of the letters of the alphabet (except for Unit 4 which introduces *k* and *q*). Coloring, cutting and pasting, and puzzle pages are typical of the activities through which your students gradually build a beginning vocabulary. The units can be completed in any order that fits your classroom activities.

In addition, five pages at the end of the book provide activities to review the letters of the alphabet. The master pages for the Pictionary and directions for their assembly are found at the end of the book.

## Unit Overview

**Teacher Notes**
Provide ideas specific for each unit theme, answers for student pages, and books, songs, poems that can be used to extend the meaning of the unit words and the unit theme.

**Theme Picture**
Illustrates the six unit words in a familiar setting, introduces consonant sounds, provides practice in following directions.

## Word Recognition
Introduces the six unit words in a "Word Bank," gives students an opportunity to use the Word Bank to match words and pictures.

## Auditory Discrimination
Practices the sound/symbol relationship for the letter introduced in this unit. A picture from the theme page illustrates the key word. (In units introducing vowels and the letter x, auditory discrimination is not developed. This page is utilized for additional letter recognition practice.)

## Word Recognition
Provides opportunity for students to trace the first letter in each of the six vocabulary words and match the words and pictures without the aid of the Word Bank.

## Activity Page
Explores the theme of the unit with crafts, puzzles, games.

## Seeing Relationships
Emphasizes the association of the words as a group through semantic mapping, classification, or simple analogies.

## Pictionary Entry Page
Contains pictures of the six unit words for students to color and paste in the appropriate box in the Pictionary.

## Activity Page
Provides creative opportunities for further exploring the theme of the unit with crafts, puzzles, or games.

## Award Certificate Page
Offers students an opportunity to complete a certificate to take home to show their parents the new words they have learned.

## Letter Recognition
Provides practice with tracing the letter introduced in the unit in capital and lower-case forms.

## Teacher Notes

**Unit Word List:**      **Unit Letter:** *M m*

| | |
|---|---|
| boy | cookies |
| desk | girl |
| milk | teacher |

### Page 7    Building Prior Knowledge

Use the theme picture to develop concepts related to school. The following questions can be used to stimulate language development:

> What kind of room does this picture show?
>
> Who is the lady in the picture?
>
> What are the children doing?
>
> What are some other things they might do at school?
>
> What letter do you see on the bulletin board?
>
> What pictures do you see there?
>
> Why do you think the teacher has placed these pictures on the bulletin board?

If your students are learning about letter-sound relationships, let them suggest other pictures the teacher might have added to the group.

### Answers for Activity Pages

**Page 8**    Students should draw a line from each word to the correct picture.

**Page 9**    Students should trace the first letter in each word and draw a line to the corresponding picture.

**Page 10**    Students should cut out the pictures at the bottom of the page and paste the following in the windows of the school: teacher, boy, girl, desk, cookies, milk.

### Page 11    Puppet Class

Additional materials: one paper bag per student
Have students:

1. Color the figure of the child to resemble themselves, and cut out along the dotted lines.
2. Paste head to the bottom of the paper bag folded flat.
3. Paste body on one side of the paper bag so that the child's mouth tucks under the lower portion of his or her head.

4. Use as a hand puppet, moving hand inside bag to open and shut the child's mouth.

After the students have assembled their puppets, they might use them in a play to explore classroom procedures.

**Page 12**    Students should trace the first letter in the words at the top of the page, color the picture, and then trace the capital and lower-case *M m*'s on the lines.

**Page 13**    Students should draw a circle around the moon, monkey, mitten, mouse.

### Page 14    M Mobile

Additional materials: string or yarn
Detail of assembly:

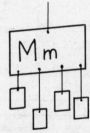

After students have assembled their mobiles, they might create similar ones using different pictures of items that begin with *m* . Or, they might make mobiles using other letters.

## Additional Unit Activities

### Books

The following books related to school might be read to the students during the completion of this unit:

> *Will I Have a Friend?* by Miriam Cohen, New York: Macmillan, 1967
>
> *Miss Nelson Is Missing!* by Harry Allard, Boston: Houghton Mifflin, 1980
>
> *Best Friends* by Miriam Cohen, New York: Collier Books, 1971
>
> *Leo, Zack, and Emmie* by Amy Ehrlich, New York: Dial Press, 1981
>
> *Crow Boy* by Taro Yashima, New York: Viking, 1955

Name _____

# School Days

After discussing the picture, have students color: teacher's dress red; girl's shirt blue; boy's shirt green; cookies brown. Then have them put an *X* on the boy's desk and draw a circle around the milk.

# Name _____

boy

cookies

desk

girl

milk

teacher

In the boxes below, have students draw a line from each word to the correct picture.

milk

boy

desk

teacher

girl

cookies

# Name _____

Have students trace the first letter of the words and then draw a line from each word to the matching picture.

milk

boy

desk

teacher

girl

cookies

Name _____

Have students cut out the boxes at the bottom of the page and paste those that could be found in school in the windows.

teacher    cookies    milk    tree

barn    desk    boy    girl

Name _____

Help students to create a paper bag puppet. See illustrated directions in the Unit 1 Teacher Notes, page 6.

# Puppet Class

Name _____

Have students trace the beginning letter in the words at the top of the page; color the picture; then trace the letters in the rows below.

# Mm Milk milk

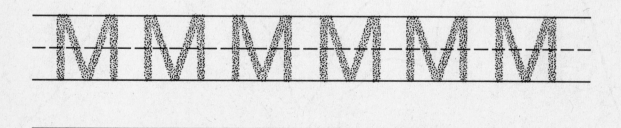

M M M M M M

m m m m m m

# Name _____

# M m

Name _____

# All M's

Direct students as they:
1. Color and cut out the pictures along the dotted lines.
2. Punch holes at circles. Tie string through holes from large "Mm" section to the small pictures. Add string at top to hang.

# Name _____

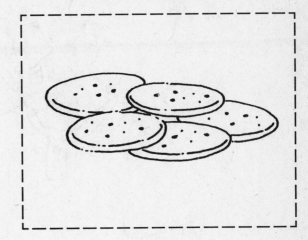

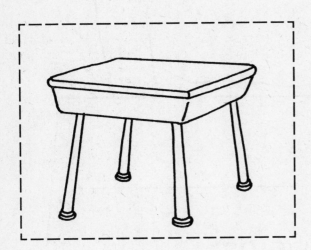

_____
Name

## can read these words:

boy            cookies        desk

girl             milk           teacher

_____
Teacher                                                        Date

## Teacher Notes

**Unit Word List:** | **Unit Letter:** *Ss*

ball      bat

school    seesaw

slide     swing

### Page 18   Building Prior Knowledge

Use the theme picture to develop concepts related to a school playground. The following questions can be used to stimulate language development:

> What do you see on the school playground that you would like to play with?
>
> Which of these playthings do we have at our school?
>
> What are some rules we should follow to play safely on a slide? A seesaw? A swing?
>
> What other playthings might be found on a school playground?

If students are learning letter-sound relationships, have them pick out all the items in the illustration that start the same as *seesaw*: sun, swing, school, slide, socks, squirrel, sneakers.

### Answers for Activity Pages

**Page 19**   Students should cut out words from bottom of page and position them under the matching pictures.

**Page 20**   Students should trace the first letter in each word and circle the matching picture.

**Page 21**   Students should paste all the pictures except the school around the word *Playthings*.

### Page 22   Playground Fun

Duplication of this page onto construction or other sturdy paper is recommended.

**Page 23**   Students should trace the first letter in the words at the top of the page, color the picture, and then trace the capital and lower case *Ss* 's on the lines.

**Page 24**   Students should draw lines from the letter *s* to the seesaw, sled, socks, sun, soap, and swing.

### Page 25   The Bouncing Ball

Students should complete the maze as shown:

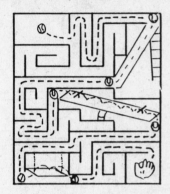

## Additional Unit Activities

**Books**

The following books and poem related to playground activities might be read to the students during the completion of this unit:

*Swinging and Swinging* by Fran Manushkin, New York, Harper & Row, 1976

*Let's Play* by Satomi Ichikawa, Philomel, 1981

*Michael Is Brave* by Helen E. Buckley, New York, Lothrop, Lee & Shepard, 1971

**Poem**

### The Swing

How do you like to go up in a swing,
     Up in the air so blue?
Oh, I do think it the pleasantest thing
     Ever a child can do!

Up in the air and over the wall,
     Till I can see so wide,
Rivers and trees and cattle and all
     Over the countryside--

Till I look down on the garden green,
     Down on the roof so brown--
Up in the air I go flying again,
     Up in the air and down!

*Robert Louis Stevenson*

17

Name _____

# On the Playground

After discussing the picture, have students color the school red. Then have them circle the playthings (ball, bat, jumprope, slide, seesaws, swings).

# Name _____

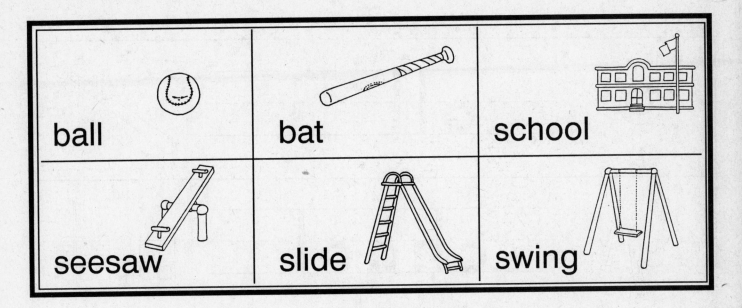

ball

bat

school

seesaw

slide

swing

Have students cut out the words at the bottom of the page and paste them below the correct pictures.

| school | ball | swing |
|--------|------|-------|
| slide | bat | seesaw |

# Name _____

Have students trace the first letter of the word in each box and circle the picture that matches the word.

 **b**all

 **s**chool

 **s**wing

 **b**at

 **s**lide

 **s**eesaw

# Name _____

Have students cut out the boxes from the bottom of the page and paste around *playthings* those that show something you play with.

Playthings

| bat | ball | slide | school | swing | seesaw |

Name _____

Direct students as they:
1. Color the picture.
2. Cut out along the dotted lines to create a puzzle.

# Playground Fun

Name _____

Have students trace the beginning letter in the words at the top of the page; color the picture; then trace the letters in the rows below.

S   Seesaw

s   seesaw

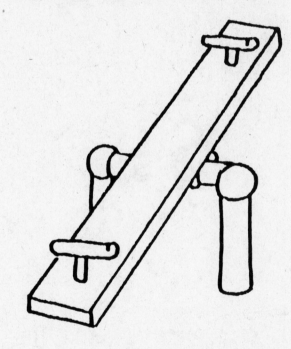

S S S S S S

s s s s s s

Name _____

Have students draw a line from the letter in the center of the circle to each object whose name begins with that letter.

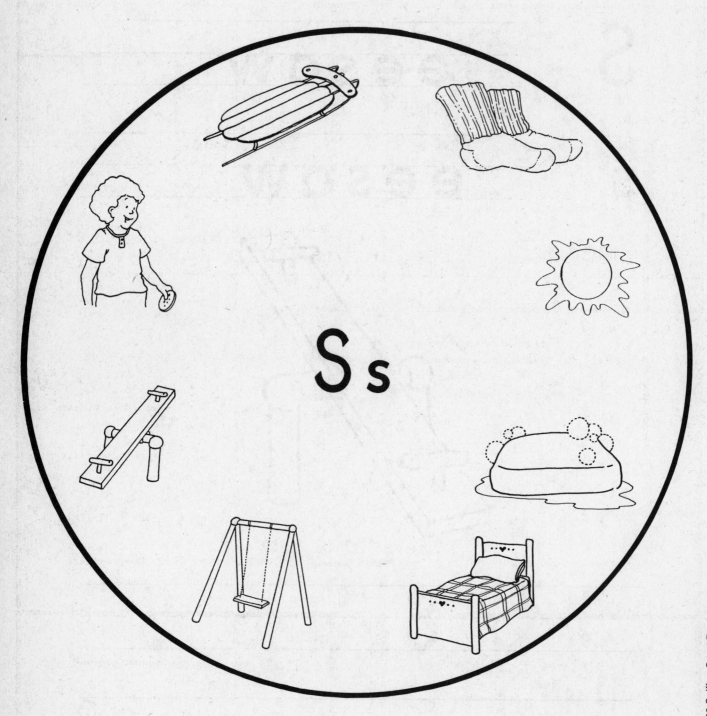

S s

# Name _____

# The Bouncing Ball

Direct students as they complete the maze, helping the ball reach the glove. The slide, seesaw, and swing will help them solve it.

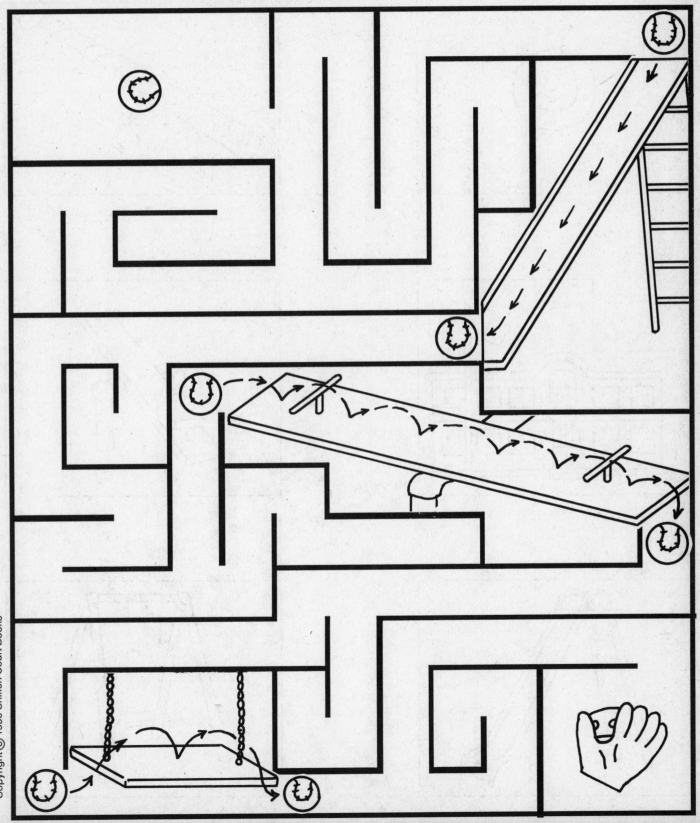

# Name _____

Have students color the pictures, cut them out along the dotted lines, and paste them into their pictionaries in the correct location.

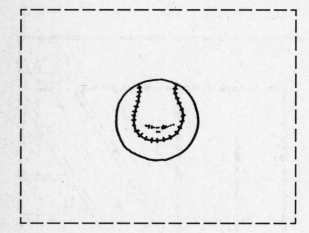

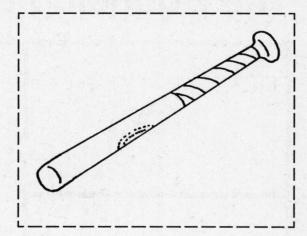

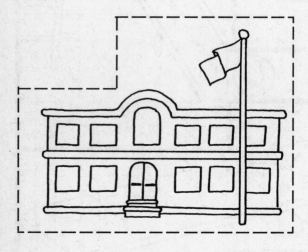

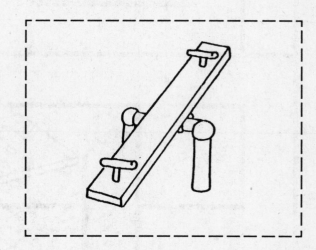

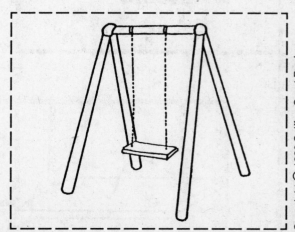

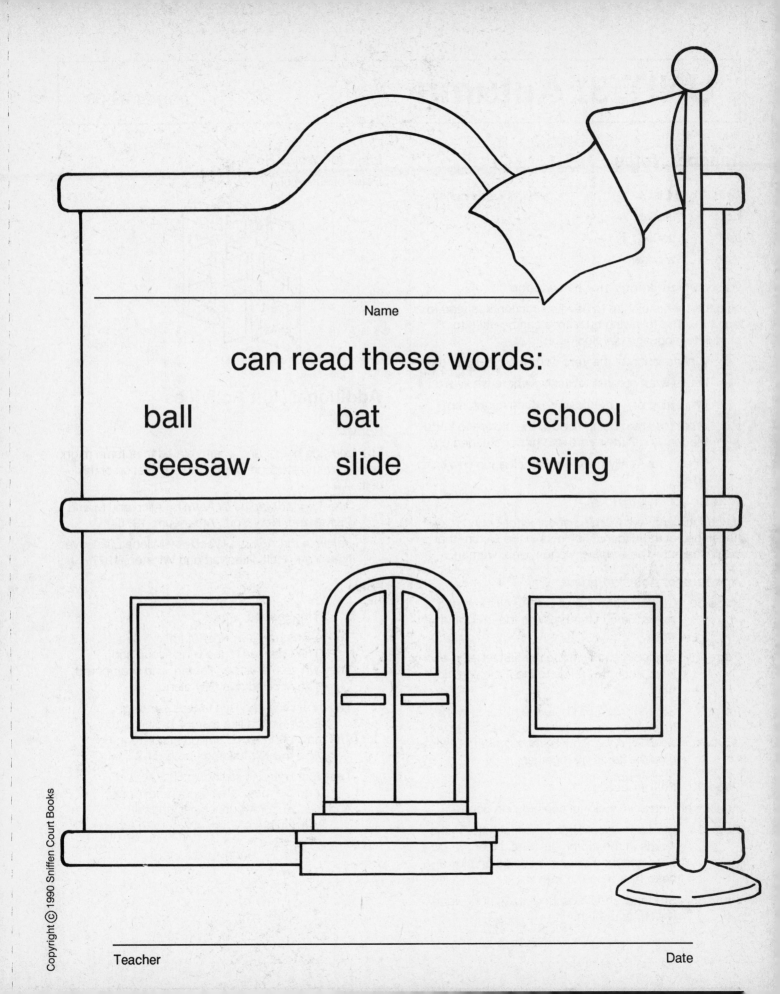

_____
Name

# can read these words:

ball   bat   school

seesaw  slide  swing

Teacher             Date

## Teacher Notes

**Unit Word List:**

| | |
|---|---|
| door | ladder |
| leaf | house |
| rake | window |

**Unit Letter:** *Ww*

### Page 29  Building Prior Knowledge

Use the theme picture to develop concepts related to autumn. The following questions can be used to stimulate language development:

What season of the year does the picture show?

Is this what autumn looks like where we live?

What kind of work has to be done in autumn?

What tools are being used in the picture to help the family get their yard and house cleaned up?

Does your family have outdoor cleanup chores to do?

Do you help? How?

If your students are learning about letter-sound relationships, let them identify objects in the picture that begin the same as *window*: wagon, web, woman.

### Answers for Activity Pages

**Page 30**  Students should cut out the pictures and paste them in the box with the matching word.

**Page 31**  Students should trace the first letter in each word and draw a line to the matching picture.

**Page 32**  Students should paste the pictures in the following order: Row 1--house,leaf; Row 2--window, door; Row 3--rake, ladder. Discuss how the items go together.

### Page 33  Falling Leaves

Additional materials: colorful construction paper

**Page 34**  Students should trace the first letter in the words at the top of the page, color the picture, and then trace the capital and lowercase *Ww* 's on the lines.

**Page 35**  Students should circle web, wagon, wand, watch, and witch.

### Page 36  Who's Home?

Detail of assembly:

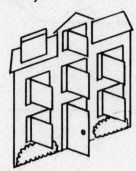

## Additional Unit Activities

### Books

The following books and poem related to autumn might be read to the students during the completion of this unit:

*The Year at Maple Hill Farm* by Alice and Martin Provensen, New York, Atheneum, 1978

*Julian in the Autumn Woods* by Milena Lukèsová New York, Holt, Rinehart and Winston, 1977

### Poem

**The Leaves**

The leaves had a wonderful frolic,
    They danced to the wind's loud song,
They whirled, and they floated, and scampered,
    They circled and flew along.

The moon saw the little leaves dancing,
    Each looked like a small brown bird.
The man in the moon smiled and listened,
    And this is the song he heard.

The North Wind is calling, is calling,
    And we must whirl round and round,
And then when our dancing is ended
    We'll make a warm quilt for the ground.

*Anonymous*

# Name _____

## Autumn

After discussing the picture, have students color: the house yellow; the door red; the leaves brown. Then have then circle the rake, draw a line under the ladder and draw curtains in the window.

# Name _____

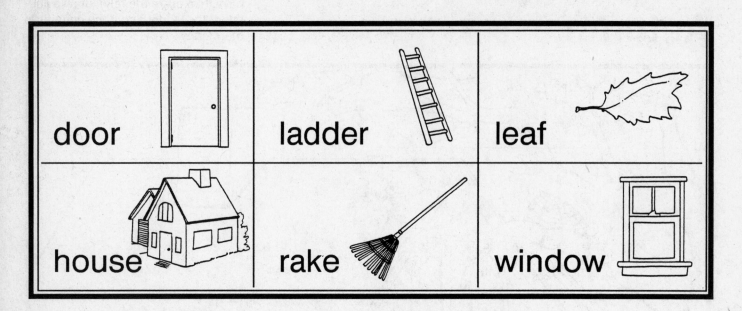

| door | ladder | leaf |
| house | rake | window |

Have students cut out the pictures below and paste them above the correct words.

| leaf | rake | door |
| house | window | ladder |

# Name _____

Have students trace the first letter of the words and draw a line from each word to the matching picture.

leaf

house

ladder

window

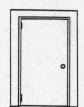

rake

door

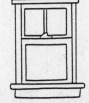

# Name _____

Have students cut out the boxes at the bottom of the page and paste each box next to the things that it goes with.

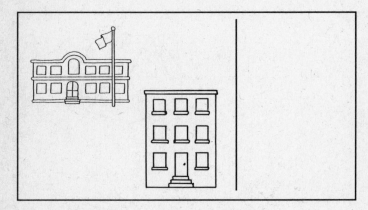

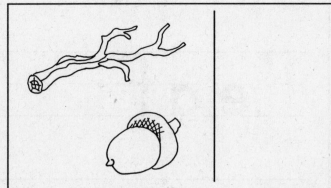

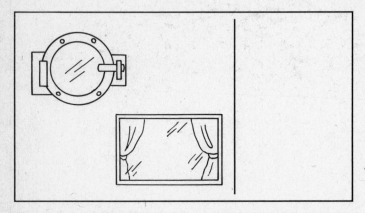

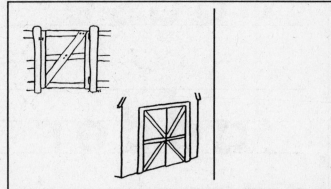

 ladder | house | leaf | rake | door | window

Name _____

# Falling Leaves

Direct students as they color the tree, adding colorful leaves to the branches and the lawn around the tree. Small snips of colorful paper may be pasted on as leaves.

Name _____

Have students trace the beginning letter in the words at the top of the page; color the picture; then trace the letters in the rows below.

**W**    Window

**w**    window

WWWWWW

w w w w w w

# Name _____

Have students circle each picture whose name begins the same as the picture in the first box.

Name _____

# Who's Home?

paste

paste

paste

paste

paste

paste

paste

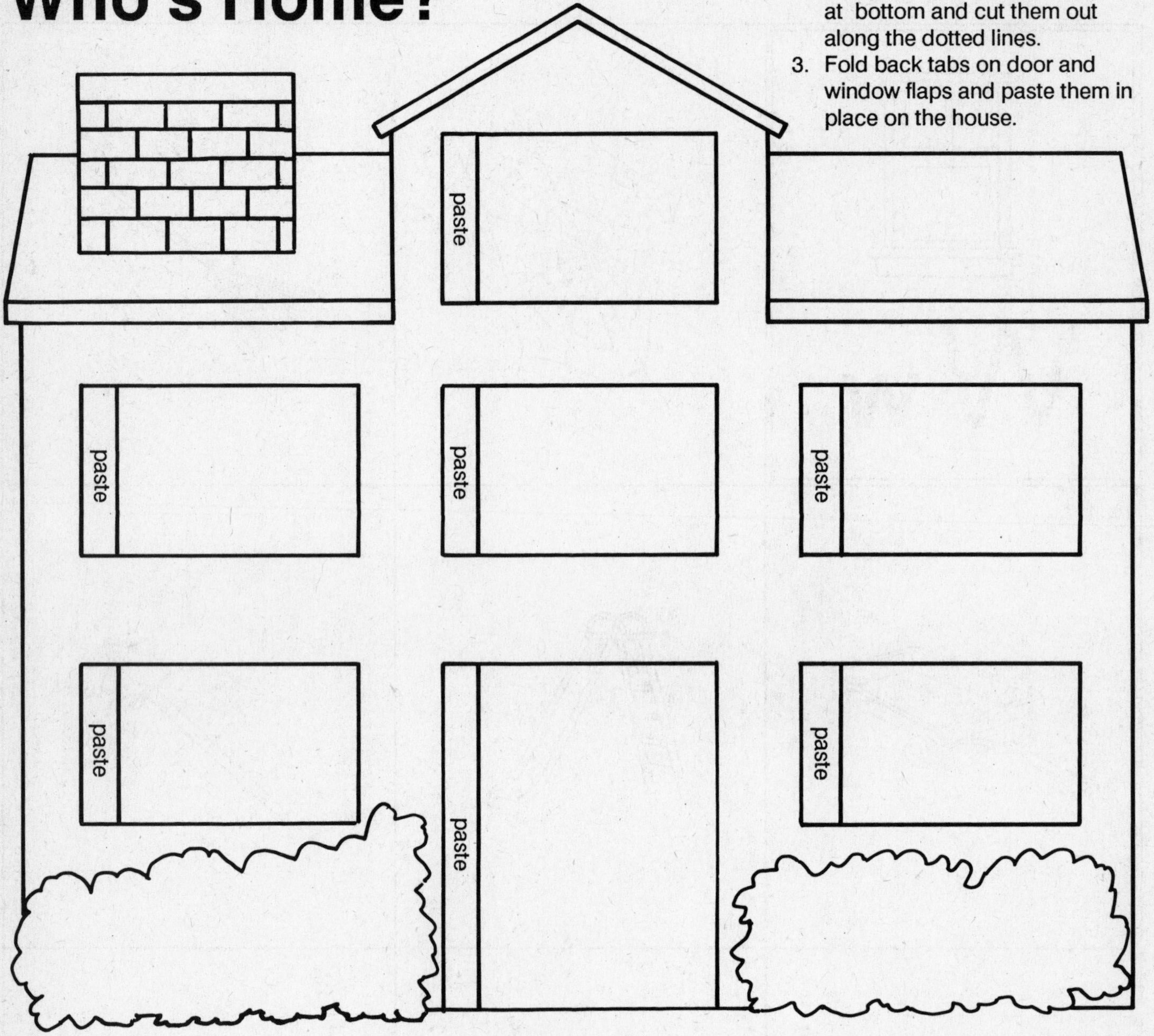

paste

# Name _____

Have students color the pictures, cut them out along the dotted lines, and paste them into their pictionaries in the correct location.

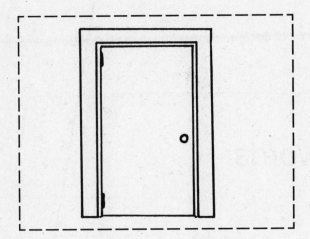

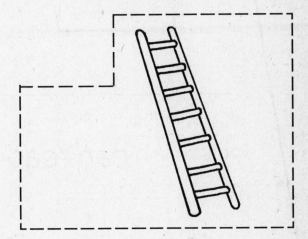

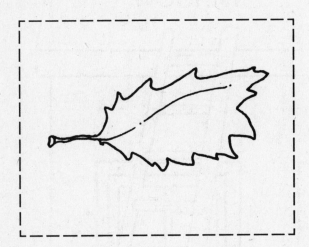

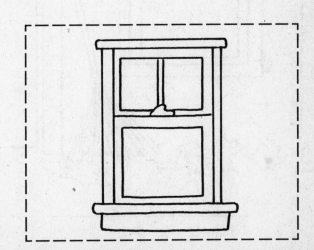

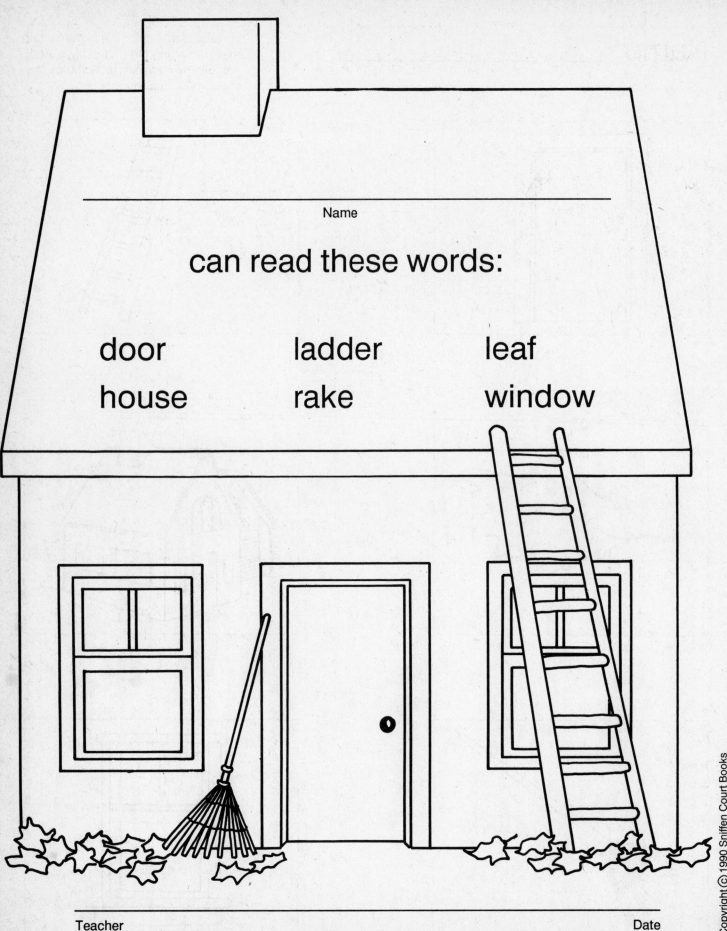

_____
Name

can read these words:

door          ladder          leaf
house         rake            window

Teacher                                              Date

## Teacher Notes

**Unit Word List:**                    **Unit Letters:** *Kk Qq*

broom       king

pumpkin     queen

spider      witch

**Page 40   Building Prior Knowledge**

Use the theme picture to develop concepts related to Halloween. The following questions can be used to stimulate language development:

> What holiday does the picture show?
>
> What are the scariest things in the picture?
>
> What are the children dressed as?
>
> Why are they carrying bags?
>
> Have you ever been trick or treating on Halloween.
>
> What kind of costume did you wear?

If students are learning letter-sound relationships, have them pick out all the items in the illustration that start the same as *king*: kitten, kangaroo.

### Answers for Activity Pages

**Page 41**   Students should draw a line from each word to the matching picture.

**Page 42**   Students should trace the first letter in each word and draw a line to the matching picture.

**Page 43**   Students should paste the pictures of the spider, witch, broom, pumpkin around the word *Halloween*.

**Page 44   Make a Crown**

Duplication of this page onto construction or other sturdy paper is recommended.

Detail of assembly:

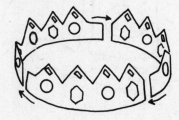

**Page 45**   Students should trace the first letter in the words at the top of the page, color the picture, and then trace the capital and lower-case *Kk*'s and *Qq*'s on the lines.

**Page 46**   Students should write *k* in the boxes with pictures of king, kite, kitten, kangaroo, kettle.

**Page 47   Pumpkin Carving**

Detail of assembly:

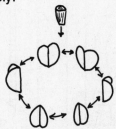

## Additional Unit Activities

**Books**

The following books and poem related to Halloween might be read to the students during the completion of this unit:

*Ghosts and Goblins: Stories for Halloween* compiled by Wilhelmina Harper, New York, Dutton, 1936

*Haunted House* by Jan Pienkowski, New York, Dutton, 1979

*The Halloween Performance* by Felicia Bond, New York, Thomas Y. Crowell, 1983

**Poem**

### The Dark House

In a dark, dark wood, there was a dark, dark house,
And in that dark, dark house, there was a dark, dark room,
And in that dark, dark room, there was a dark, dark cupboard,
And in that dark, dark cupboard, there was a dark, dark shelf,
And in that dark, dark shelf, there was a dark, dark box,
And in that dark, dark box, there was a GHOST!

*Anonymous*

Name _____

# Halloween

After discussing the picture, have students color: the pumpkin orange, the broom red, the spider black. Then have them draw a line under the king and queen and circle the witch.

# Name _____

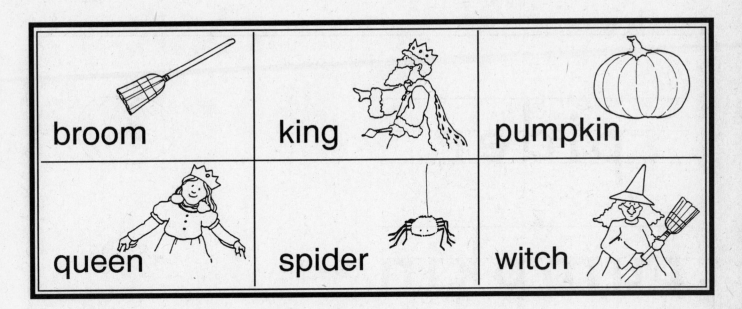

In the boxes below, have students draw a line from each word to the correct picture.

Name _____

spider

pumpkin

witch

queen

king

broom

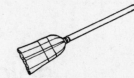

Name _____

Have students cut out the boxes at the bottom of the page and paste around *Halloween* those boxes that are related to it.

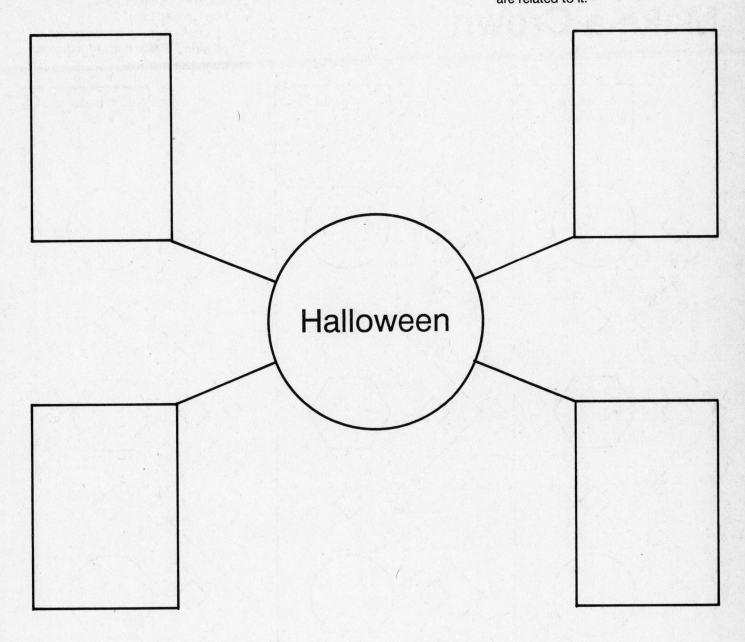

Halloween

spider  witch  broom  milk  desk  pumpkin

# Name _____

# Make a Crown

Direct students as they:
1. Color the crown strips and cut them out along the dotted lines.
2. Paste strips end to end, overlapping tabs.
3. Fit crown around head and cut off extra. Paste ends together to complete crown.

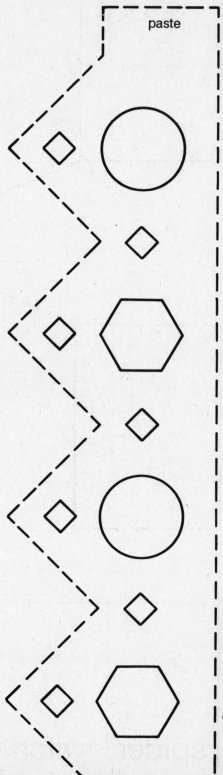

paste  paste  paste

Name _____

Have students trace the beginning letter in the words at the top of the page; color the picture; then trace the letters in the rows below.

**Kk**  King  k

**Qq**  Queen  q

K K K k k k

Q Q Q q q q

# Name _____

Have students trace the *k* below the king and then write *k* in each box that has a picture of something whose name starts like *king*.

k

Name _____

# Pumpkin Carving

Direct students as they:
1. Cut out circles and color both sides orange. Fold all the circles in half along fold line.
2. Paste one folded half circle exactly aligned with another half circle. Continue with remaining circles.
3. Turn stack of half circles around to paste last half circle to the first, forming a ball.
4. Color, cut out, and paste the stem to the top of the pumpkin.

# Name _____

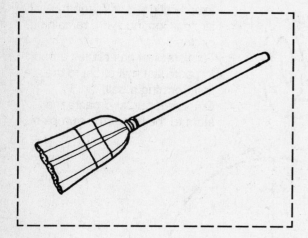

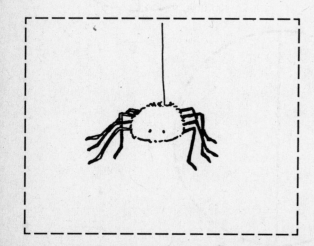

Name

can read these words:

broom       king       pumpkin
queen       spider     witch

Teacher

Date

## Teacher Notes

**Unit Word List:**    **Unit Letter:** *Ll*

cat          dog
lamp         radio
telephone    television

### Page 51    Building Prior Knowledge

Use the theme picture to develop concepts related to family activities at home. The following questions can be used to stimulate language development:

What part of a house or an apartment do you think this is?

What are some of the things you could do in this room?

If you were in this room now, what would you like to do?

What other rooms might be found in this house?

How would they be used?

If students are learning letter-sound relationships, have them pick out all the items in the illustration that start the same as *lamp*: lemon, leaf, lightning, letter, lion.

### Answers for Activity Pages

**Page 52**    Students should cut out the pictures at the bottom of the page and paste them in the box with the matching words.

**Page 53**    Students should trace the first letter in each word and circle the matching picture.

**Page 54**    Students should draw pictures of a cat and a television and paste the cat beside the dog and the television beside the radio.

### Page 55    Pop-Up Book

Detail of assembly:

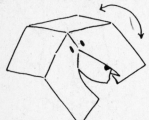

1. Cut out book along dotted lines and color the pictures.

2. Fold along the vertical fold and cut along dotted lines to create the dog's snout.

3. Fold along the snout fold and then unfold the book.

4. Fold along the horizontal fold to create book cover.

5. Push pop-up to the inside of the book and reverse the vertical and snout folds as necessary to complete the pop-up book.

After the students have assembled their books, let them make up a dog story and tell it to the class.

**Page 56**    Students should trace the first letter in the words at the top of the page, color the picture, and then trace the capital and lowercase *Ll*'s on the lines.

**Page 57**    Students should draw a circle around the lion, lobster, ladder, and lamb.

### Page 58    TV Time

Detail of assembly:

Fold paper in half perpendicular to slits and then cut across fold along dotted line to make slits.

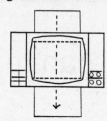

## Additional Unit Activities

### Books

The following books and poems related to activities at home might be read to the students during the completion of this unit:

*In Our House* by Anne Rockwell, New York, Harper & Row, Publishers, 1985

*Staying Home Alone on a Rainy Day* by Chichiro Iwasaki, New York, McGraw-Hill, 1969

*Anybody Home?* by Aileen Fisher, New York, Thomas Y. Crowell, 1980

*You Ought to See Herbie's House* by Doris Herold Lund, New York, Franklin Watts, 1973

### Poems

*A House Is a House for Me* by Mary Ann Hoberman, New York, Viking, 1978

# Name _____

## At Home

After discussing the picture, have students color: the dog brown; the cat black. Then have them circle the television and radio and draw a line under the lamp and telephone.

Name _____

| cat | dog | lamp |
| radio | telephone | television |

Have students cut out the pictures below and paste them above the correct words.

| telephone | dog | radio |
| lamp | television | cat |

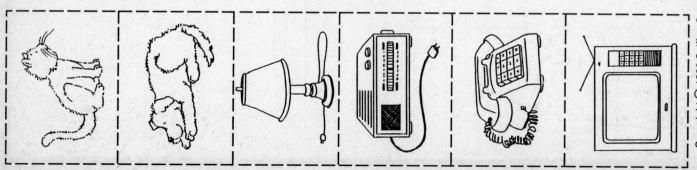

# Name _____

Have students trace the first letter of the word in each box and circle the picture that matches the word.

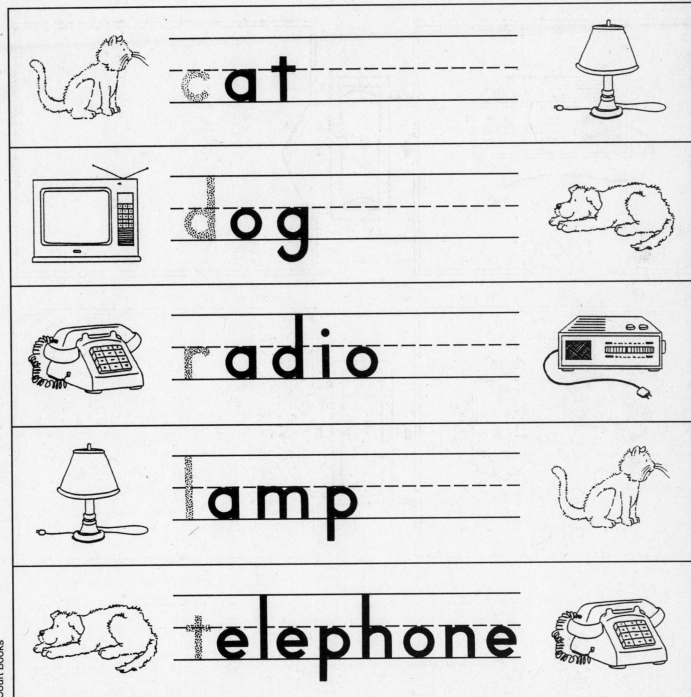

cat

dog

radio

lamp

telephone

television

# Name _____

Have students draw pictures to match the words in the boxes at the bottom of the page. Then have them cut out the boxes and paste them beside the objects they go with.

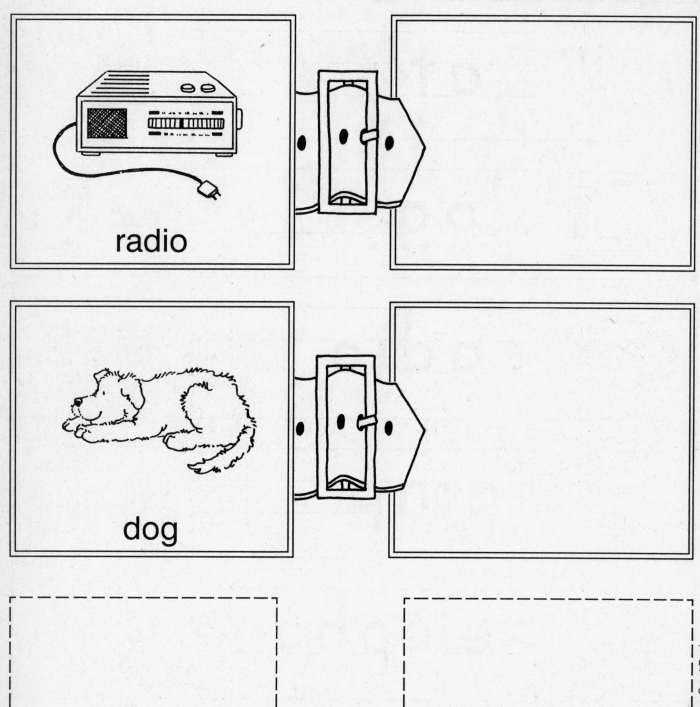

radio

dog

cat

television

# Name _____

Help students to create a pop-up book. See illustrated directions in the Unit 5 Teacher Notes, page 50.

# Pop-Up Book

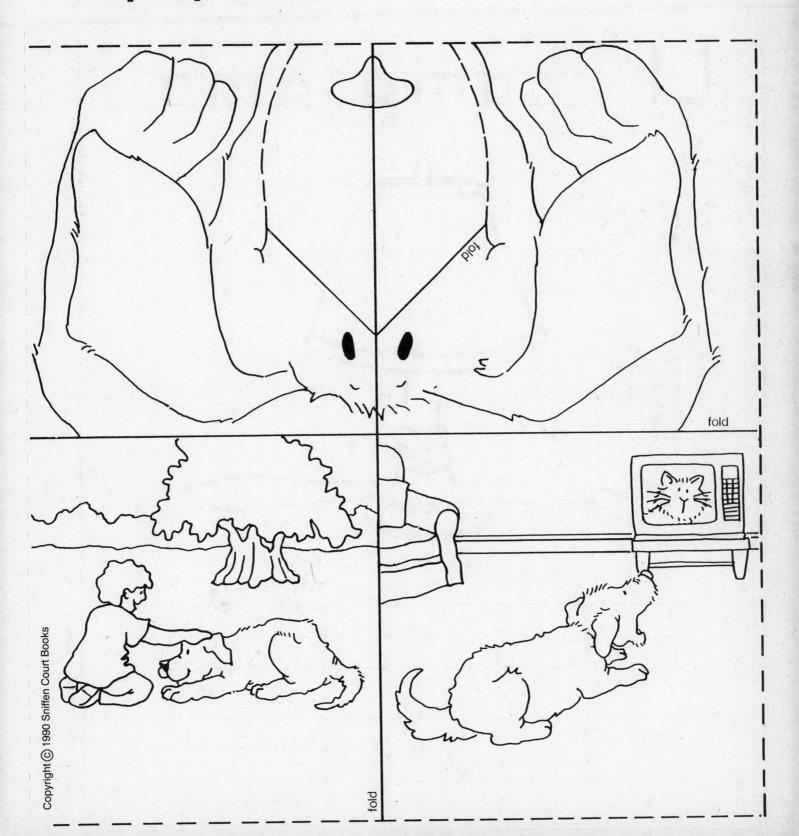

fold

fold

fold

Name _____

Have students trace the beginning letter in the words at the top of the page; color the picture; then trace the letters in the rows below.

L l   Lamp lamp

L L L L L L

l l l l l l

# Name _____

Have students circle the objects that begin with the same sound as the objects at the top of the page.

## L l

 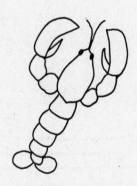 

# Name _____

# TV Time

Direct students as they:

1. Color the television and the strip of scenes.
2. Cut out strip and cut slits in the television along the dotted lines.
3. Slide strip through top slit from the back of the page and then into the bottom slit. Slide strip up and down to view different "programs."

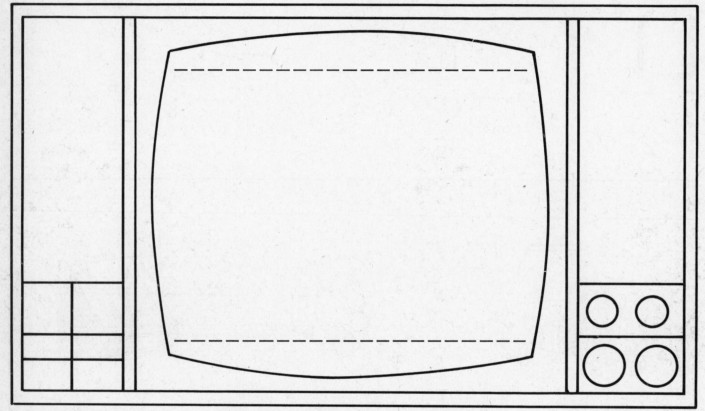

# Name _____

Have students color the pictures, cut them out along the dotted lines, and paste them into their pictionaries in the correct location.

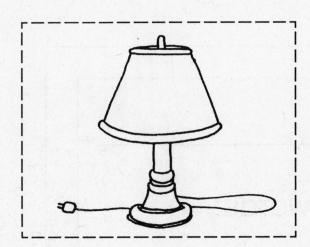

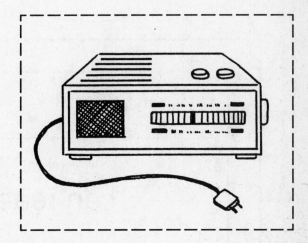

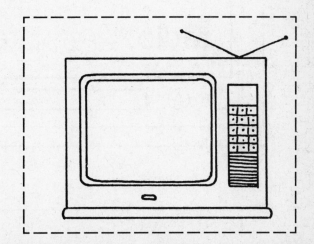

_____

Name

## can read these words:

| cat | dog | lamp |
| radio | telephone | television |

## Teacher Notes

**Unit Word List:**          **Unit Letter:** *Ff*

| | |
|---|---|
| apron | bowl |
| fork | jar |
| pan | spoon |

### Page 62   Building Prior Knowledge

Use the theme picture to develop concepts related to kitchen activities. The following questions can be used to stimulate language development:

> What is happening in the picture?
>
> What room is this?
>
> What do you think the father in this picture is cooking?
>
> Have you ever cooked anything for your family?
>
> How did you do it?
>
> Do you see anything in the picture that you would have in your kitchen?

If students are learning letter-sound relationships, have them pick out all the items in the illustration that start the same as *fork*: fish, frog, four, five.

### Answers for Activity Pages

**Page 63**   Students should cut out the words at the bottom of the page and paste them in the box with the matching picture.

**Page 64**   Students should trace the first letter in each word and draw a line to the matching picture.

**Page 65**   Students should paste all the pictures on the pockets on the apron except "slide."

### Page 66   What Is It?

Students should have connected the dots as indicated below:

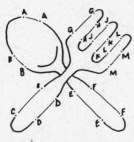

**Page 67**   Students should trace the first letter in the words at the top of the page, color the picture, and then trace the capital and lowercase *Ff* 's on the lines.

**Page 68**   Students should draw a line from *Ff* to the pictures of the fork, flag, frog, and 4.

### Page 69   Where Is It?

Students should have circled the items as indicated below:

## Additional Unit Activities

### Books

The following books related to cooking might be read to the students during the completion of this unit:

> *"I Can't," Said the Ant* by Polly Cameron, New York, Putnam, 1961
>
> *Hattie Be Quiet, Hattie Be Good* by Dick Gackenbach, New York, Harper & Row, 1977
>
> *A Worm for Dinner* by Ned Delaney, Boston, Houghton Mifflin, 1977

# Name _____

## Kitchen Helper

After discussing the picture, have students color the apron red. Then have them circle the fork and spoon and put an *X* on the bowl, pan and jar.

Name _____

| apron | bowl | fork |
| jar | pan | spoon |

Have students cut out the words at the bottom of the page and paste them below the correct pictures.

| fork | bowl | apron |
| spoon | pan | jar |

**Name** _____

Have students trace the first letter of the words and draw a line from each word to the matching picture.

bowl

apron

fork

pan

spoon

jar

Name _____

Have students cut out the boxes at the bottom of the page and paste in the pockets of the apron those that tell about things in the kitchen.

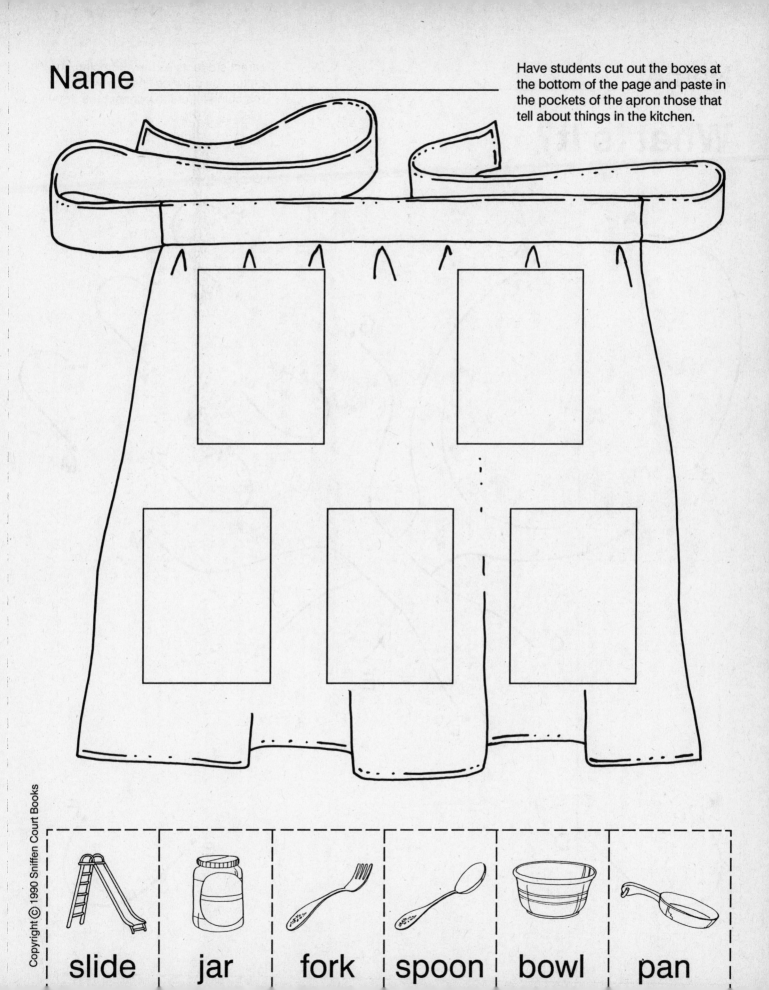

| slide | jar | fork | spoon | bowl | pan |

# Name _____

Direct students as they complete the picture by drawing lines between matching letters to connect the dots.

# What Is It?

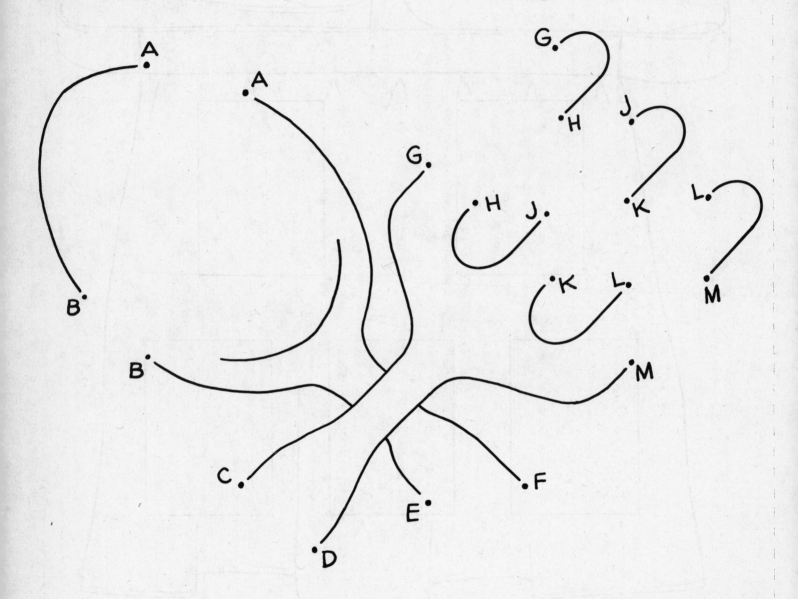

Name _____

Have students trace the beginning letter in the words at the top of the page; color the picture; then trace the letters in the rows below.

# Ff Fork fork

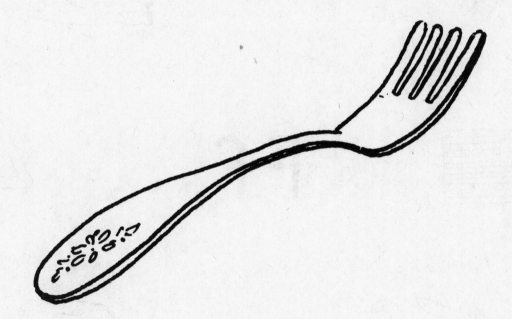

F F F F F

f f f f f

Name _____

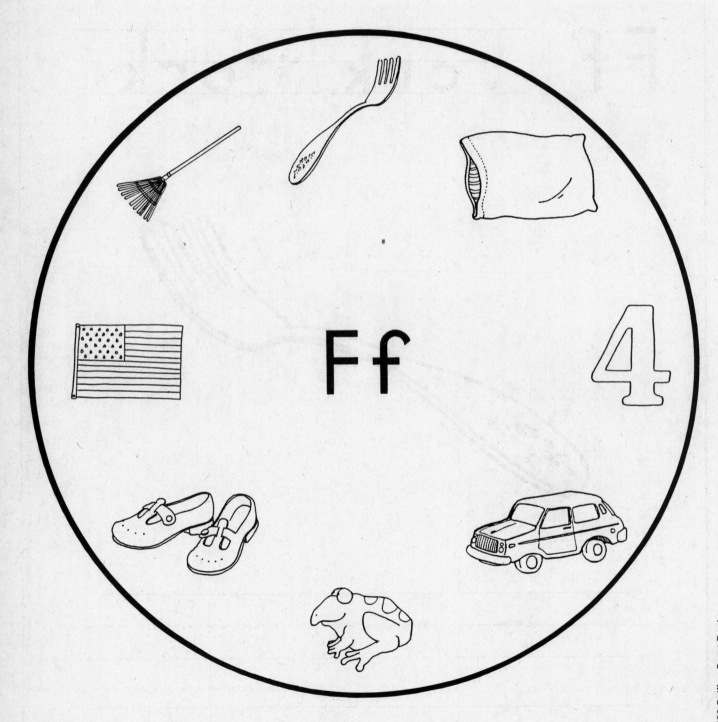

Have students draw a line from the letter in the center of the circle to each object whose name begins with that letter.

Ff

# Name _____

# Where Is It?

Have students find the items shown below that are hidden in the picture and circle them. Then, have students color the picture.

# Name _____

Have students color the pictures, cut them out along the dotted lines, and paste them into their pictionaries in the correct location.

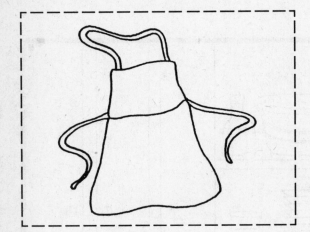

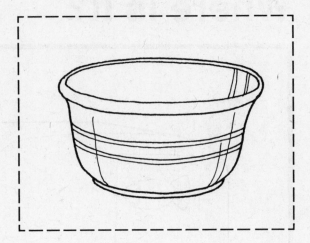

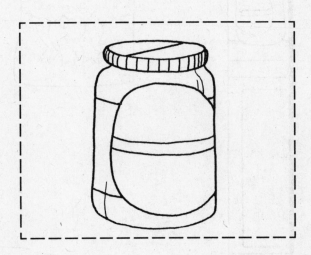

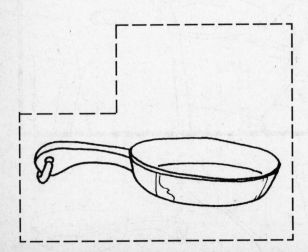

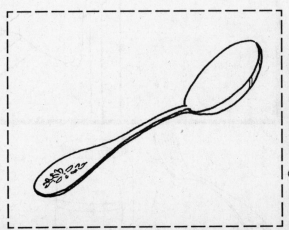

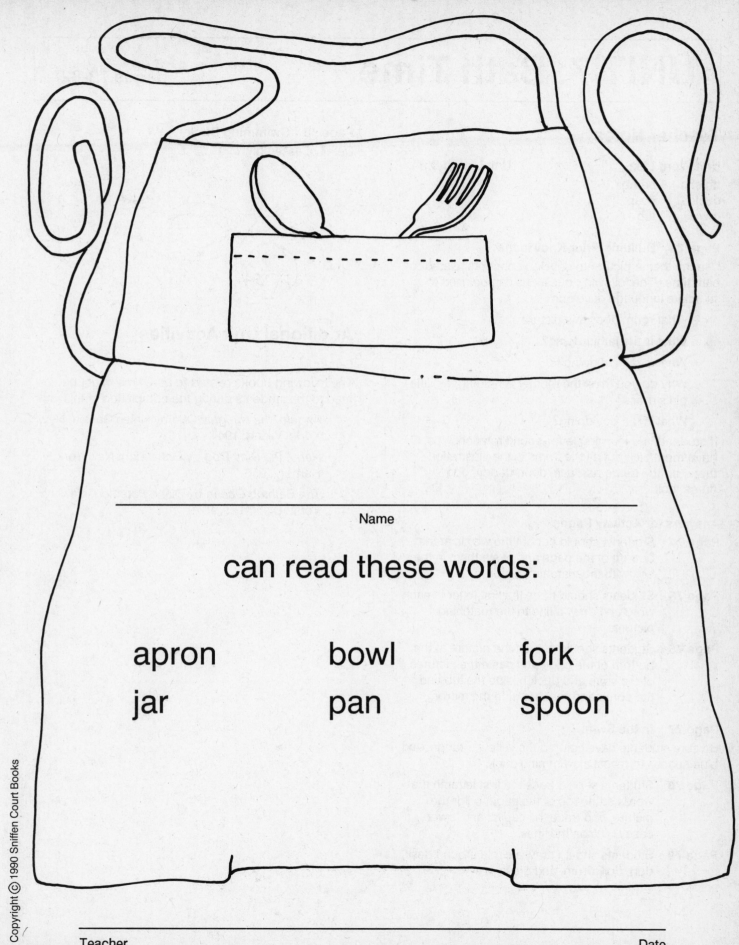

_____
Name

## can read these words:

apron        bowl        fork

jar           pan         spoon

_____
Teacher                                               Date

## Teacher Notes

### Unit Word List:

brush    comb
duck     soap
towel    tub

### Unit Letter: *D d*

### Page 73   Building Prior Knowledge

Use the theme picture to develop concepts related to bath time. The following questions can be used to stimulate language development:

> What room does this picture show?
>
> What is the father doing?
>
> What is the girl doing?
>
> Why do you think the mother is holding the little girl's dress?
>
> What is the boy doing?

If students are learning letter-sound relationships, have them pick out all the items in the illustration that start the same as *duck*: door, daddy, dog, dress, doll.

### Answers for Activity Pages

**Page 74**   Students should cut out the words at the bottom of the page and paste them in the box with the matching pictures.

**Page 75**   Students should trace the first letter in each word and draw a line to the matching picture.

**Page 76**   Students should cut out the picture at the bottom of the page and paste the pictures of the soap and duck beside the tub and the comb and brush beside the mirror.

### Page 77   In the Swim

Be sure students have colored the yellow, orange, and blue spaces to reveal a swimming duck.

**Page 78**   Students should trace the first letter in the words at the top of the page, color the picture, and trace the capital and lower-case *D d*'s on the lines.

**Page 79**   Students should draw a circle around desk, dog, doll, drum, and dress.

### Page 80   Swimming Duck

Detail of assembly:

## Additional Unit Activities

### Books

The following books related to bath time might be read to the students during the completion of this unit:

> *Angelo, the Naughty One* by Helen Garrett, New York: Viking, 1944
>
> *Harry, the Dirty Dog* by Gene Zion, New York: Harper, 1956
>
> *The Bathtub Ocean* by Diane Paterson, New York: Dial Press, 1979

Name _____

# Bath Time

After discussing the picture, have students color: the duck yellow; the tub blue. Then have them put an *X* on things used when taking a bath (soap, towel) and underline things used to fix hair (comb, brush).

# Name _____

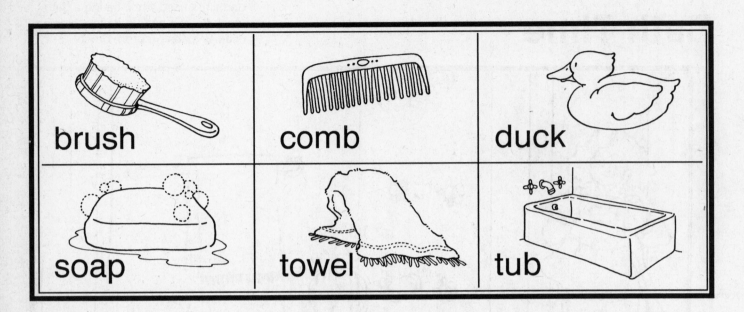

brush

comb

duck

soap

towel

tub

Have students cut out the words at the bottom of the page and paste them below the correct pictures.

| comb | brush | tub |
| --- | --- | --- |
| soap | towel | duck |

# Name _____

Have students trace the first letter of the words and then draw a line from each word to the matching picture.

brush

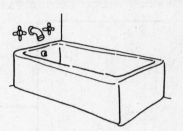

comb

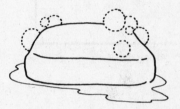

tub

soap

towel

duck

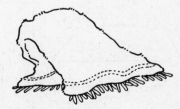

Name _____

Have students cut out the boxes at the bottom of the page and paste them beside the objects they go with.

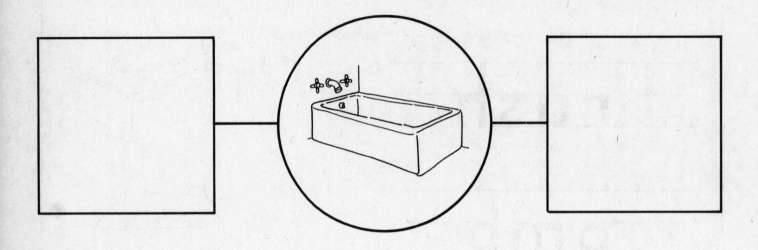

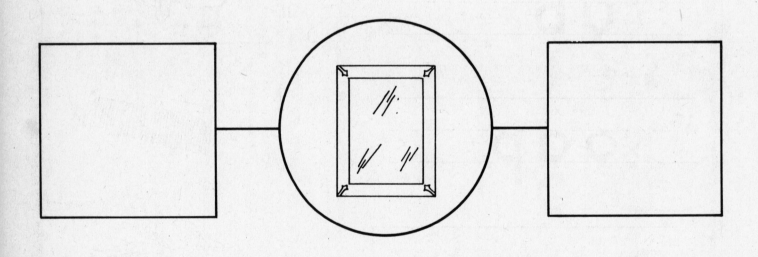

soap     comb     duck     brush

Name _____

Direct students to reveal the hidden picture by coloring the spaces as follows: X, blue; O, orange; dots, yellow.

# In the Swim

Name _____

Have students trace the beginning letter in the words at the top of the page; color the picture; then trace the letters in the rows below.

# Dd Duck duck

D D D D D D

d d d d d d

# Name _____

Have students circle each picture whose name begins the same as the picture in the first box.

Name _____

# Swimming Duck

Direct students as they:
1. Color the duck and feet wheel.
2. Cut out duck and feet wheel along dotted lines.
3. Push paper fastener through the X on the duck and then through the X on the feet wheel.
4. When rolled along on edge, the duck's feet move to simulate walking.

X

# Name _____

Have students color the pictures, cut them out along the dotted lines, and paste them into their pictionaries in the correct location.

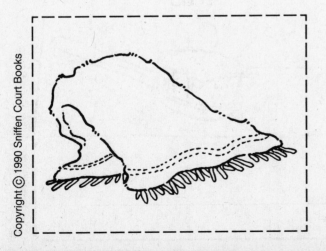

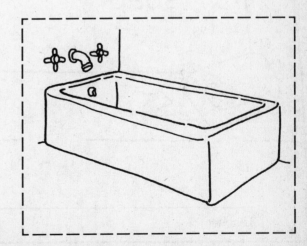

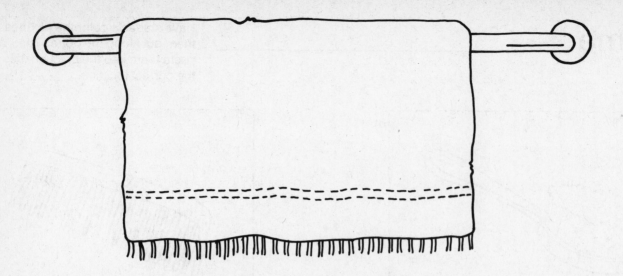

_____
Name

## can read these words:

brush            comb            duck

soap             towel           tub

_____
Teacher                                    Date

## Teacher Notes

**Unit Word List:**                    **Unit Letter:** *B b*

bear          bed
blanket       doll
moon          pillow

### Page 84    Building Prior Knowledge

Use the theme picture to develop concepts related to bedtime. The following questions can be used to stimulate language development:

> What kind of room do you see in the picture?
>
> Do you see anything here that you have in your bedroom?
>
> Which of the things in this room might a child take to bed?
>
> Do you have anything special that you like to take to bed with you?
>
> What are some of the things you do to get ready for bed?

If students are learning letter-sound relationships, have them pick out all the items in the illustration that start the same as *bear*: bat, basket, ball, bus, boat, book, blanket, bed.

### Answers for Activity Pages

**Page 85**    Students should draw a line from each word to the matching picture.

**Page 86**    Students should trace the first letter of each word and circle the matching picture.

**Page 87**    Students should cut out the pictures at the bottom of the page and paste bear, pillow, doll, and blanket in the boxes around the bed.

### Page 88    Bedtime Sky

Additional materials: clothes hanger, string, glitter
Detail of assembly:

**Page 89**    Students should trace the first letter in the words at the top of the page, color the picture, and then trace the capital and lower-case *B b*'s on the lines.

**Page 90**    Students should draw a circle around the book, blanket, bird, and boat.

### Page 91    Talking Bear

Additional materials: paper fasteners
Duplication of this page onto construction or other sturdy paper is recommended.

Detail of assembly:

Fold paper in half perpendicular to slit and then cut across fold along dotted lines to make slit.

## Additional Unit Activities

### Books

The following books, poems, and songs related to bedtime might be enjoyed by the students during the completion of this unit:

> *Bedtime for Frances* by Russell Hoban, New York: Harper & Row, 1960
>
> *Corduroy* by Don Freeman, New York: Viking Press, 1968
>
> *Goodnight Moon* by Margaret Wise Brown, New York: Harper & Row, 1947

### Songs

> *Teddy Bears' Picnic*
> *Rock-a-bye Baby*
> *Twinkle, Twinkle, Little Star*

### Poems

Help children recite and pantomime the traditional jump rope rhyme:

> Teddy Bear, Teddy Bear
> Turn around, round, round.
>
> Teddy Bear, Teddy Bear
> Touch the ground, ground, ground.
>
> Teddy Bear, Teddy Bear
> Climb the stairs, stairs, stairs.
>
> Teddy Bear, Teddy Bear
> Turn out the light, light, light.
>
> Teddy Bear, Teddy Bear
> Say good night, night, night.

Name _____

# Bedtime

After discussing the picture, have students color: the bed red; the blanket blue; the doll's dress green; the moon yellow; the pillow orange; the bear brown.

# Name _____

Have students identify each picture and word in the Word Bank.

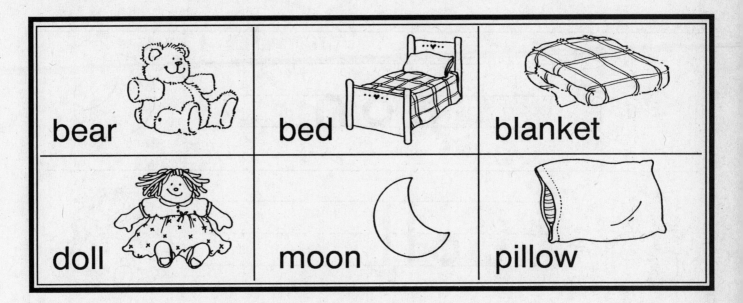

bear     bed     blanket

doll     moon     pillow

In the boxes below, have students draw a line from each word to the correct picture.

pillow        bear

doll        bed

blanket        moon

# Name _____

Have students trace the first letter of the word in each box and circle the picture that matches the word.

moon

doll

blanket

bear

pillow

bed

# Name _____

Have students cut out the boxes at the bottom of the page and paste around the bed those that show things they might take to bed.

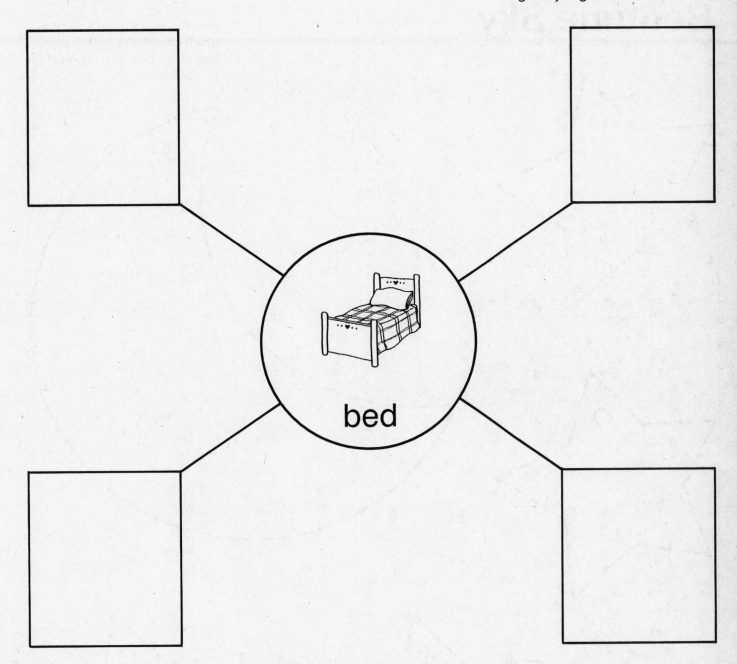

bed

bear | moon | pillow | doll | blanket

Name _____

# Bedtime Sky

Direct students as they:
1. Color and cut out the shapes along the dotted lines. Use glue to add glitter to the shapes.
2. Punch holes at circles. Tie one end of string through holes and attach other end to wire hanger.
3. Suspend mobile from hook of the hanger.

Name _____

Have students trace the beginning
letter in the words at the top of the
page; color the picture; then trace
the letters in the rows below.

# Bb Bear bear

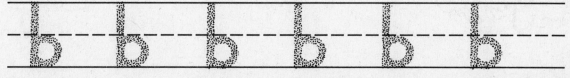

B B B B B B B

b b b b b b b

# Name _____

Have students circle the objects that begin with the same sound as the objects at the top of the page.

# B b

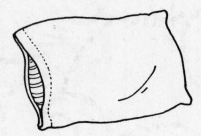
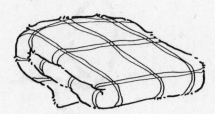

# Name _____

# Talking Bear

Direct students as they:
1. Color the bear.
2. Cut out the bear, ear-tongue strip, and slit for mouth along the dotted lines.
3. Insert a paper fastener through the X on the bear's nose and then through the X on the ear-tongue strip.
4. Slip tongue through mouth slit. Move ear and tongue will slide back and forth.

ear

X

tongue

# Name _____

Have students color the pictures, cut them out along the dotted lines, and paste them into their pictionaries in the correct location.

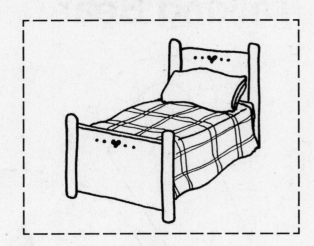

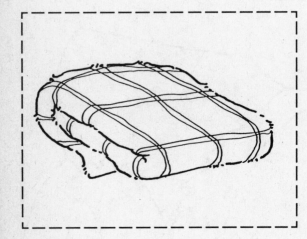

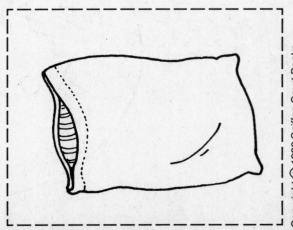

_____
Name

# can read these words:

bear        bed        blanket

doll        moon       pillow

_____        _____
Teacher        Date

# UNIT 9: Thanksgiving

## Teacher Notes

**Unit Word List:**

brother    corn

daddy    mommy

sister    turkey

**Unit Letter:** *Cc*

### Page 95   Building Prior Knowledge

Use the theme picture to develop concepts related to Thanksgiving. The following questions can be used to stimulate language development:

> What holiday might this family be celebrating?
>
> What members of the family are shown in the picture?
>
> What are they having for dinner?
>
> How does your family celebrate Thanksgiving?
>
> Who fixes Thanksgiving dinner for your family?
>
> Do you help?
>
> Do other members of your family get together with you for Thanksgiving dinner?

If students are learning letter-sound relationships, have them pick out all the items in the illustration that start the same as *corn*: cookies, carrots, cake, cat, candy, clock.

### Answers for Activity Pages

**Page 96**   Students should cut out the pictures at the bottom of the page and paste them in the boxes with the matching words.

**Page 97**   Students should trace the first letter in each word and draw a line to the matching picture.

**Page 98**   Students should paste *mommy, daddy, sister, brother* below the frames around *Family* and draw pictures to match each word.

### Page 99   A Family Tree

Students should include any members of their family they wish.

**Page 100**   Students should trace the first letter in the words at the top of the page, color the picture, and then trace the capital and lowercase *Cc* 's on the lines.

**Page 101**   Students should trace the *c* under the corn. Then have them write *c* under the pictures of coat, cake, carrot, cat, and comb.

### Page 102   Turkey Feathers

Duplication of this page onto construction or other sturdy paper is recommended.

Detail of assembly:

## Additional Unit Activities

### Books

The following books and poems related to Thanksgiving might be read to the students during the completion of this unit:

*Sometimes It's Turkey--Sometimes It's Feathers* by Lorna Balian, New York, Abingdon Press, 1973

*Mousekin's Thanksgiving* by Edna Miller, New York, Prentice Hall, 1985

*Oh, What a Thanksgiving* by Steven Kroll, New York, Scholastic, 1988

### Poems

*Make a Circle Keep Us In: Poems for a Good Day* by Arnold Adoff, New York: Delacorte Press, 1975

#### Thanksgiving

Over the river and through the wood,
> To grandfather's house we go;
>> The horse knows the way
>> To carry the sleigh
> Through the white and drifted snow.

Over the river and through the wood--
> Oh, how the wind does blow!
>> It stings the toes
>> And bites the nose,
> As over the ground we go.

Over the river and through the wood
> Trot fast, my dapple-gray!
>> Spring over the ground,
>> Like a hunting-hound!
> For this is Thanksgiving day!

*Traditional*

# Name _____

## Thanksgiving

After discussing the picture, have students circle all the members of the family (daddy, mommy, brother, sister), draw a line under the turkey, and put an *X* on the corn.

# Name _____

Have students identify each picture and word in the Word Bank.

| | | |
|---|---|---|
| brother | corn | daddy |
| mommy | sister | turkey |

Have students cut out the pictures below and paste them above the correct words.

| | | |
|---|---|---|
| sister | daddy | turkey |
| corn | brother | mommy |

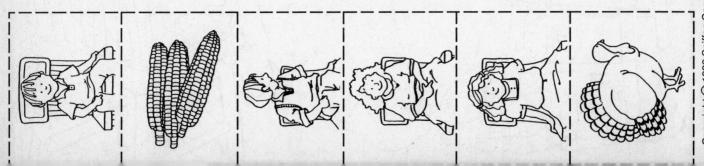

# Name _____

Have students trace the first letter of the words and draw a line from each word to the matching picture.

daddy

turkey

corn

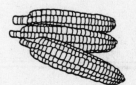

mommy

sister

brother

# Name _____

Have students cut out the boxes at the bottom of the page and paste those describing family members below the frames. Then have them draw appropriate pictures in the frames.

Family

corn    mommy    brother

turkey    sister    daddy

Name _____

# A Family Tree

Direct students as they draw and color a picture of themselves in the larger box and other members of their families in the smaller boxes.

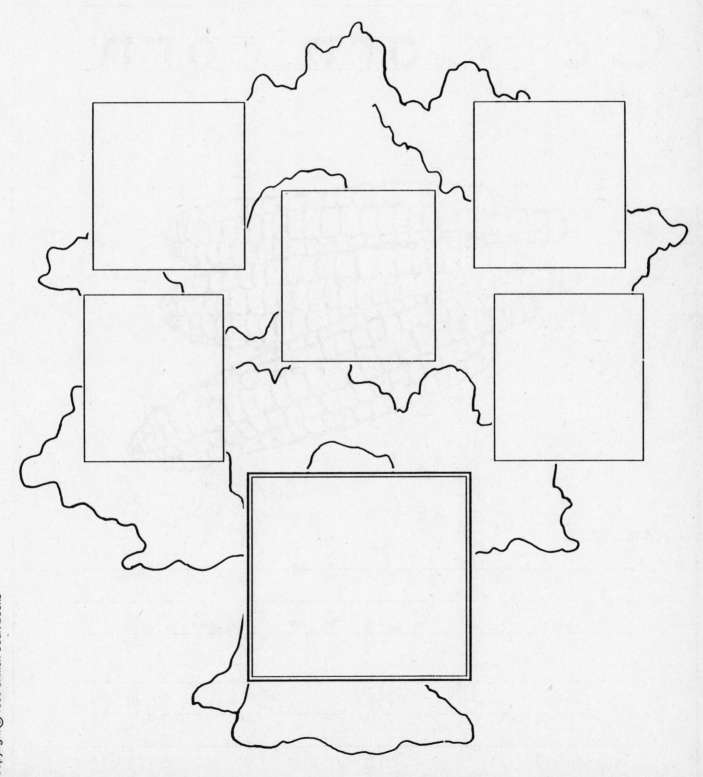

Name _____

Have students trace the beginning letter in the words at the top of the page; color the picture; then trace the letters in the rows below.

C c Corn corn

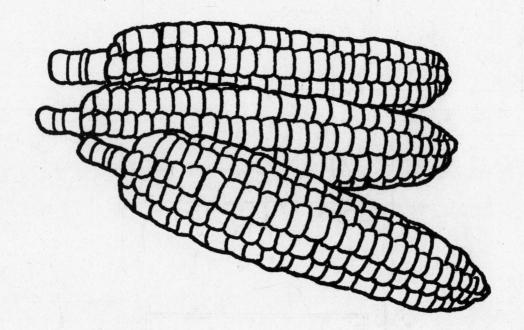

C C C C C C

c c c c c c

# Name _____

# Name _____

# Turkey Feathers

Direct students as they:
1. Color the turkey and its feathers. Cut them out along the dotted lines.
2. Paste the feathers on the turkey to create a colorful tail.
3. Fold large tabs back so turkey can stand upright.

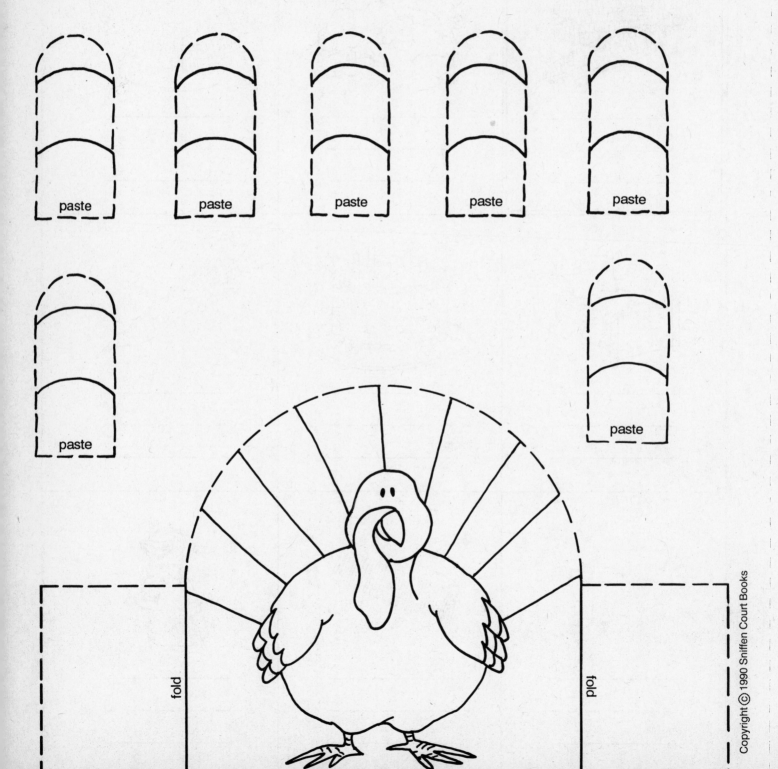

paste

paste

paste

paste

paste

paste

paste

fold

fold

# Name _____

Have students color the pictures, cut them out along the dotted lines, and paste them into their pictionaries in the correct location.

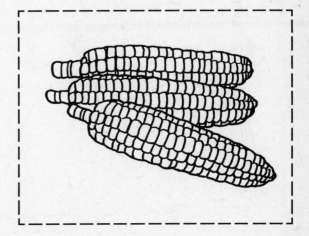

_____
Name

# can read these words:

brother     corn     daddy

mommy     sister     turkey

_____

_____
Teacher                         Date

## Teacher Notes

**Unit Word List:**

**Unit Letter:** *Ii*

boots    coat

ice    mitten

sled    snowman

### Page 106 Building Prior Knowledge

Use the theme picture to develop concepts related to wintertime. The following questions can be used to stimulate language development:

What are the children doing?

What season does this picture show?

What kind of clothes do children wear in winter?

Is this the kind of winter we have in our part of the country?

What is our winter like?

If you were with these children, what would you like to be doing?

### Answers for Activity Pages

**Page 107** Students should draw a line from each word to the matching picture.

**Page 108** Students should trace the first letter in each word and draw a line to the matching picture.

**Page 109** Students should cut out the pictures at the bottom of the page and paste the coat beside the jacket, the boots beside the shoes, the mitten beside the glove, and the sled beside the skiis.

### Page 110 Make a Snowman

Detail of assembly:

**Page 111** Students should trace the first letter in the words at the top of the page, color the picture, and then trace the capital and lowercase *Ii*'s on the lines.

**Page 112** Students should circle the letters as follows:

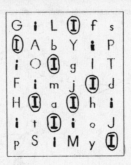

### Page 113 A Sled Ride

Detail of assembly:

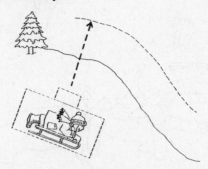

Fold paper in half perpendicular to slit and then cut across fold along dotted lines to make slit.

## Additional Unit Activities

### Books

The following books related to winter might be read to the students during the completion of this unit:

*White Snow, Bright Snow* by Alvin Tresselt, New York, Lothrop, 1947

*The Snowy Day* by Ezra Jack Keats, New York, Viking, 1962

*A Walk in the Snow* by Phyllis S. Busch, New York, J.P. Lippincott, 1971

*A Walk on a Snowy Night* by Judy Delton, New York, Harper & Row 1982

*Happy Winter* by Karen Gundersheimer, New York, Harper & Row, 1982

Name _____

# Winter

After discussing the picture, have students color: the boots red; the coats yellow; the mittens blue. Then have them put an X on the ice and circle the sleds and the snowman.

# Name _____

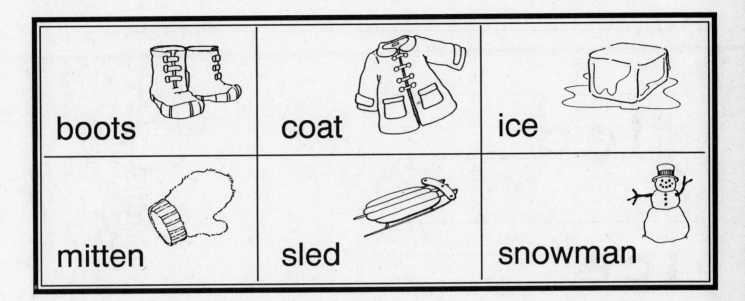

In the boxes below, have students draw a line from each word to the correct picture.

Name _____

Have students trace the first letter of the words and then draw a line from each word to the matching picture.

sled

ice

coat

boots

snowman

mitten

Name _____

Have students cut out the boxes at the bottom of the page and paste each beside an object that is similar.

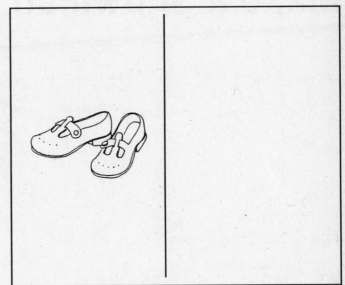

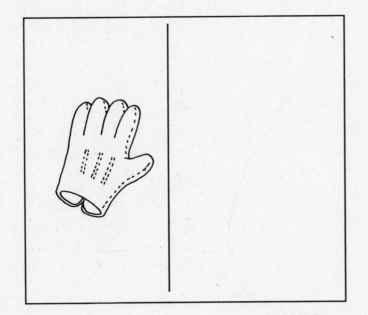

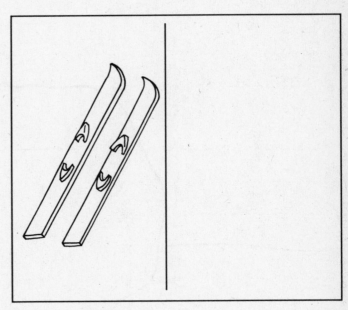

boots          coat          mitten          sled

# Name _____

# Make a Snowman

Direct students as they color the snowman, cutting and pasting in place the objects at the bottom of the page as desired.

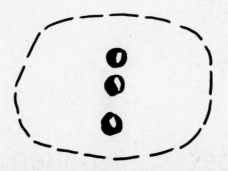

Name _____

Have students trace the beginning
letter in the words at the top of the
page; color the picture; then trace
the letters in the rows below.

# Ii   Ice  ice

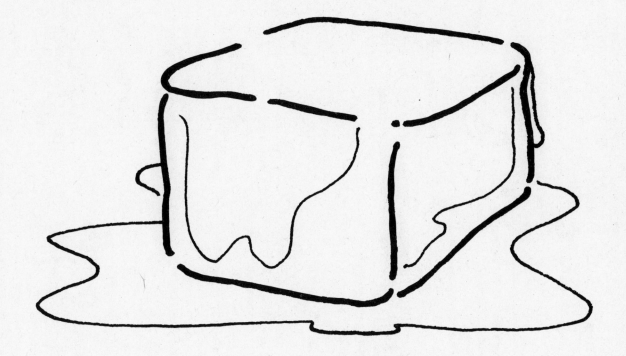

I I I I I

i i i i i

Have students color all the *I*'s and *i*'s in the letter search. Then, have students circle the capital *I*'s.

G i L I f s

I A b Y i P

i O I g I T

F i m j I d

H I a I h i

i t I i o J

p S i M y I

Name _____

# A Sled Ride

Have students look at the picture clues for winter words and write words in the boxes to build a snow hill. Word clues are in the box below. Then, direct students as they:

1. Color and cut out the sled along the dotted line. Fold tab down.
2. Cut slit in page along dotted line.
3. Slip sled tab into slit and slide sled down the hill.

boots     mitten

coat     sled

ice     snowman

# Name _____

Have students color the pictures, cut them out along the dotted lines, and paste them into their pictionaries in the correct location.

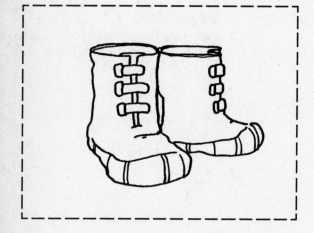

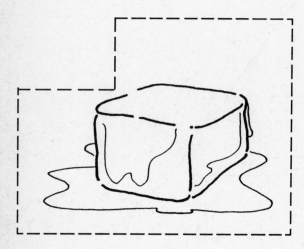

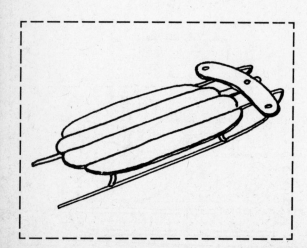

_____
Name

## can read these words:

boots          coat          ice

mitten        sled          snowman

_____
Teacher                                        Date

115

Make Your Own Pictionary

## Teacher Notes

**Unit Word List:**    **Unit Letter:** *Tt*

airplane    bicycle

bus    car

train    truck

### Page 117 Building Prior Knowledge

Use the theme picture to develop concepts related to transportation. The following questions can be used to stimulate language development:

> What different ways of traveling can you find on this page?
>
> What is your favorite way to travel?
>
> What is the fastest way to travel that is shown in this picture?
>
> Can you tell us about a time you travelled by airplane? Train? Bus? Car? Bike?

If students are learning letter-sound relationships, have them pick out all the items in the illustration that start the same as *train*: truck, T-shirt, turtle, tree.

### Answers for Activity Pages

**Page 118** Students should cut out the words at the bottom of the page and paste them in the box with the matching picture.

**Page 119** Students should trace the first letter in each word and draw a circle around the matching picture.

**Page 120** Students should paste *train, bicycle, truck, bus, car, airplane* around the wheel.

### Page 121 Let's Go

Detail of assembly:

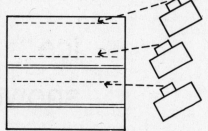

Fold paper in half perpendicular to slits and then cut across fold along dotted lines to make slits.

**Page 122** Students should trace the first letter in each word at the top of the page, color the picture, and then trace the capital and lower-case *Tt* 's on the lines.

**Page 123** Students should draw a line from *Tt* to train, T-shirt, truck, tree, 2.

### Page 124 On the Bus

Duplication of this page onto construction or other sturdy paper is recommended.

Detail of assembly:

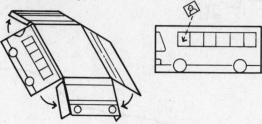

## Additional Unit Activities

### Books

The following books related to city street scenes might be read to the students during the completion of this unit:

> *And to Think That I Saw It on Mulberry Street* by Dr. Seuss, Vanguard, 1937
>
> *Make Way For Ducklings* by Robert McCloskey, New York, Viking, 1941
>
> *Taxi: A Book of City Words* by Betsy Maestro, Boston, Clarion Books, 1989
>
> *Red Light, Green Light* by Golden MacDonald, New York, Doubleday, 1944

### Song

### The Wheels of the Bus Go Round and Round

> The wheels on the bus go round and round
> Round and round, round and round.
> The wheels on the bus go round and round
> All through the town.
>
> The driver on the bus says, "Step to the rear!
> Step to the rear! Step to the rear!"
> The driver on the bus says, "Step to the rear!"
> All through the town.

Other verses:
> The people on the bus go up and down.
> The kids on the bus go yakkity-yak.
> The wipers on the bus go swish, swish, swish.

*Anonymous*

Name _____

After discussing the picture, have students find and circle all the ways of traveling shown in the picture.

# Street Scene

RAIL ROAD CROSSING

# Name _____

Have students identify each picture and word in the Word Bank.

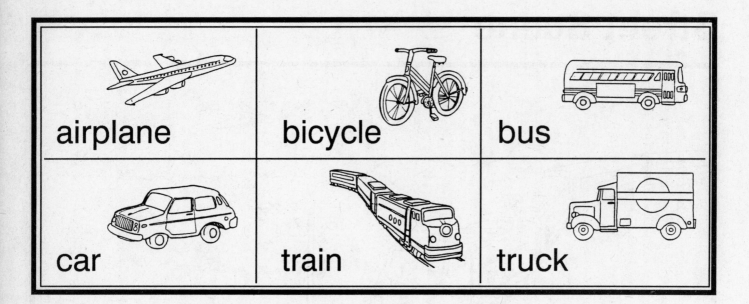

| airplane | bicycle | bus |
| --- | --- | --- |
| car | train | truck |

Have students cut out the words at the bottom of the page and paste them below the correct pictures.

| train | car | bus |
| --- | --- | --- |
| bicycle | truck | airplane |

Copyright © 1990 Sniffen Court Books

# Name _____

Have students trace the first letter of the word in each box and circle the picture that matches the word.

 airplane

 train

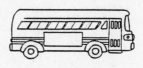 truck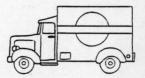

 bicycle

 bus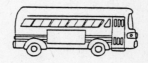

 car

Name _____

Have students cut out the words at the bottom of the page and paste those that describe objects with wheels around the large wheel.

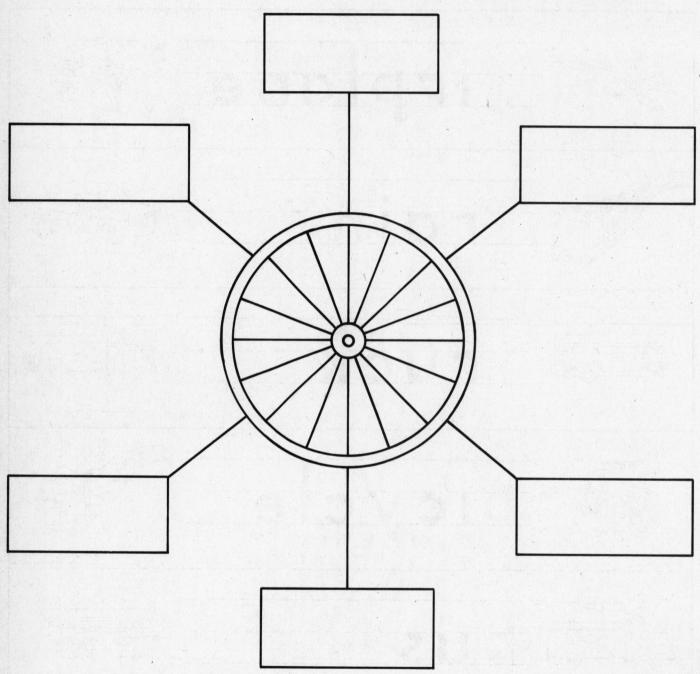

| train | turkey | bicycle | truck |
| bus | pumpkin | car | airplane |

# Name _____

# Let's Go

Direct students as they:
1. Color and cut out the vehicles at the bottom of the page along the dotted lines. Fold down tabs.
2. Color and cut slits in picture along the dotted lines.
3. Slip tabs into slits and slide vehicles back and forth.

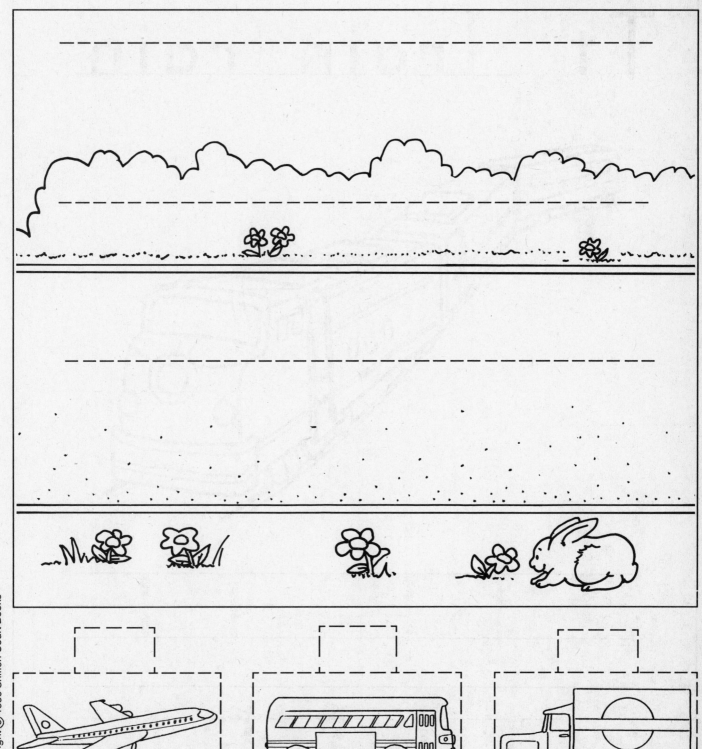

Name _____

Have students trace the beginning
letter in the words at the top of the
page; color the picture; then trace
the letters in the rows below.

# T t  Train train

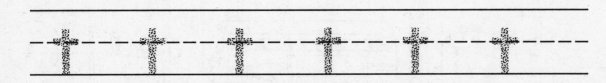

Name _____

Have students draw a line from the letter in the center of the circle to each object whose name begins with that letter.

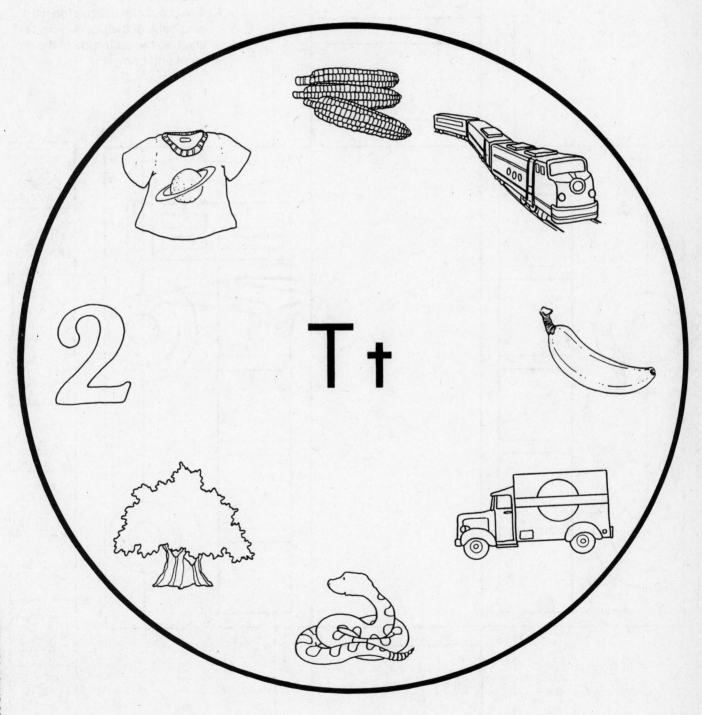

Name _____

# On the Bus

Direct students as they:
1. Color the bus and the people.
2. Cut out the bus and the people along the dotted lines, pasting the people in place in the windows of the bus.
3. Fold front, back, and sides of the bus down.
4. Fold back the tabs on the front and back of the bus and paste them to the underside of the bus front and back.

# Name _____

Have students color the pictures, cut them out along the dotted lines, and paste them into their pictionaries in the correct location.

_____
Name

## can read these words:

| airplane | bicycle | bus |
| car | train | truck |

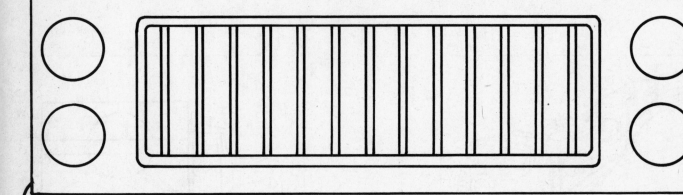

_____                    _____
Teacher                                                          Date

## Teacher Notes

**Unit Word List:**   **Unit Letter:** *Xx*

| | |
|---|---|
| baby | bottle |
| doctor | nurse |
| sweater | x-ray |

### Page 128 Building Prior Knowledge

Use the theme picture to develop concepts related to a visit to the doctor. The following questions can be used to stimulate language development:

Who do you see in the picture?

What is the doctor doing?

Does the baby look happy?

What baby things do you see in the picture?

Can you tell about a time when you visited the doctor?

### Answers for Activity Pages

**Page 129** Students should cut out the pictures at the bottom of the page and paste them in the box with the matching words.

**Page 130** Students should trace the first letter in each word and draw a line to the matching picture.

**Page 131** Students should paste the bottle and sweater under *baby* and nurse and x-ray under *doctor*.

### Page 132 Word Search

Students should circle the words as indicated below:

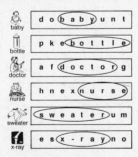

**Page 133** Students should trace the first letter in each word at the top of the page, color the picture, and then trace the capital and lower-case *Xx*'s on the lines.

**Page 134** Students should draw a circle around the *Xx*'s as shown below:

### Page 135 Memory Game

Have students paste the cut-out cards on cardboard or construction paper to make them more durable and less transparent.

## Additional Unit Activities

### Books

The following books related to a visit to the doctor might be read to the students during the completion of this unit:

*Come to the Doctor, Harry* by Mary Chalmers, New York, Harper & Row, 1981

*Dr. De Soto* by William Steig, New York, Farrar, 1982

*My Doctor* by Harlow Rockwell, New York, Macmillan, 1973

*My Dentist* by Harlow Rockwell, New York, Greenwillow/Morrow, 1975

Name _____

# Doctor's Office

After discussing the picture, have students color the baby's sweater blue. Then have them draw a line under the doctor and the nurse, draw a line from the baby to the bottle, and put an X on the x-ray.

# Name _____

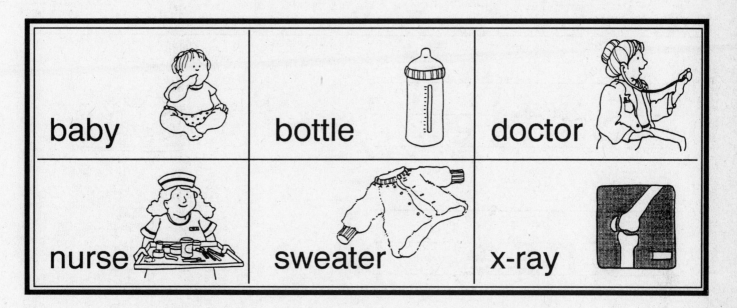

baby | bottle | doctor

nurse | sweater | x-ray

Have students cut out the pictures below and paste them above the correct words.

| bottle | doctor | x-ray |
|--------|--------|-------|
| baby | nurse | sweater |

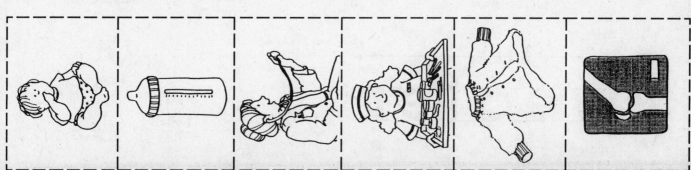

Name _____

Have students trace the first letter of
the words and draw a line from each
word to the matching picture.

bottle

nurse

baby

doctor

x-ray

sweater

# Name _____

Have students cut out the boxes at the bottom of the page and paste the things a baby needs and the things a doctor needs in the appropriate spaces.

baby

doctor

nurse

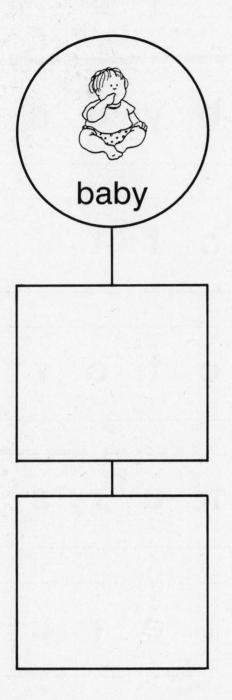

x-ray

bottle

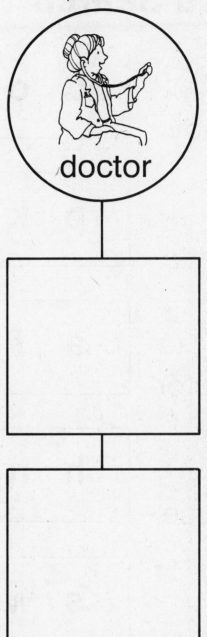

sweater

# Name _____

Have students study each clue picture and word. Then have them locate and circle the hidden word in each row that matches the clue.

# Word Search

baby

| d o b a b y u n t |

bottle

| p k e b o t t l e |

doctor

| a f d o c t o r g |

nurse

| h n e x n u r s e |

sweater

| s w e a t e r u m |

x-ray

| e s x - r a y n o |

**Name** _____

# X x   X-ray x-ray

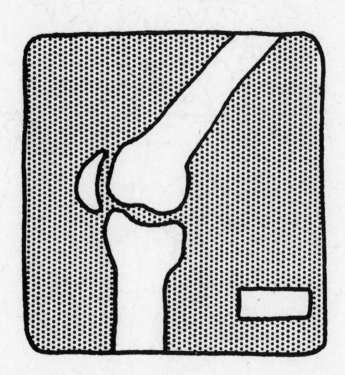

X   X   X   X   X   X

X   X   X   X   X   X

Name _____

# Name _____

## Memory Game

Have students color and cut out the cards along the dotted lines.
To play the game, mix and turn cards face down. In turn, each player turns up two cards. If the cards match, the player keeps them. If not, cards are turned over and play continues.

baby

doctor

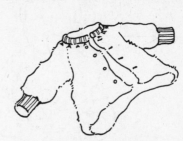

sweater

baby

doctor

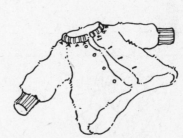

sweater

bottle

nurse

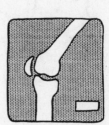

x-ray

bottle

nurse

x-ray

# Name _____

Have students color the pictures, cut them out along the dotted lines, and paste them into their pictionaries in the correct location.

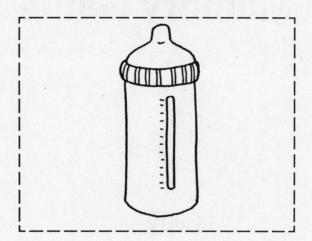

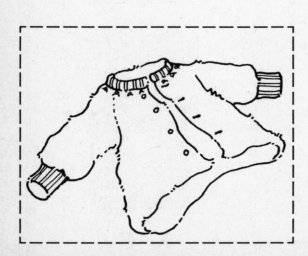

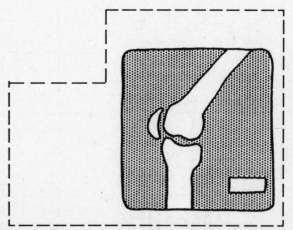

_____
Name

## can read these words:

baby          bottle          doctor
nurse         sweater         x-ray

_____
Teacher                                    Date

## Teacher Notes

**Unit Word List:**          **Unit Letter:** *Pp*

carrot     fish

kitten     puppy

rabbit     turtle

### Page 139 Building Prior Knowledge

Use the theme picture to develop concepts related to pets. The following questions can be used to stimulate language development:

>What kind of store do you see in this picture?

>Have you been to a pet store?

>Which one of the pets in this picture would you like to have?

>If you had to feed these pets, what would you give each of them?

>Tell about a pet you have at home.

If students are learning letter-sound relationships, have them pick out all the items in the illustration that start the same as *puppy*: pillow, parrot, pencil, paper.

### Answers for Activity Pages

**Page 140** Students should cut out the words at the bottom of the page and paste them in the box with the matching picture.

**Page 141** Students should trace the first letter in each word and draw a line to the matching picture.

**Page 142** Students should paste the fish, kitten, puppy, rabbit, turtle around *Pet Shop*.

### Page 143 Pencil Play

Detail of assembly:

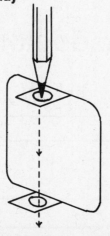

**Page 144** Students should trace the first letter in the words at the top of the page, color the picture, and then trace the capital and lowercase *Pp*'s on the lines.

**Page 145** Students should draw a circle around the pan, pants, pie, paste, pig, and pillow.

### Page 146 Pet Bookmarks

Duplication of this page onto construction or other sturdy paper is recommended.

## Additional Unit Activities

### Books

The following books related to pets might be read to the students during the completion of this unit:

>*Rebecka* by Frank Asch, New York, Harper & Row, 1972

>*At Mary Bloom's* by Aliki, New York, Greenwillow, 1976

>*Momo's Kitten* by Mitsu Yashima and Taro Yashima, New York, Viking, 1961

### Poem

**A B C D Goldfish**

A B C D goldfish?

L M N O goldfish.

O S A R goldfish.

*Anonymous*

# Name _____

# Pet Shop

After discussing the picture, have students color: the fish red, the kitten orange, the puppy black, the turtle green, and the rabbit brown. Then have them put an X on the carrot.

Fish
$2.50 each

**Name** _____

carrot     fish     kitten

puppy     rabbit     turtle

Have students cut out the words at the bottom of the page and paste them below the correct pictures.

| carrot | rabbit | puppy |
| --- | --- | --- |
| fish | kitten | turtle |

# Name _____

Have students trace the first letter of the words and then draw a line from each word to the matching picture.

turtle

kitten

fish

puppy

rabbit

carrot

# Name _____

Have students cut out the boxes at the bottom of the page and paste those around Pet Shop that show things to buy at a pet shop.

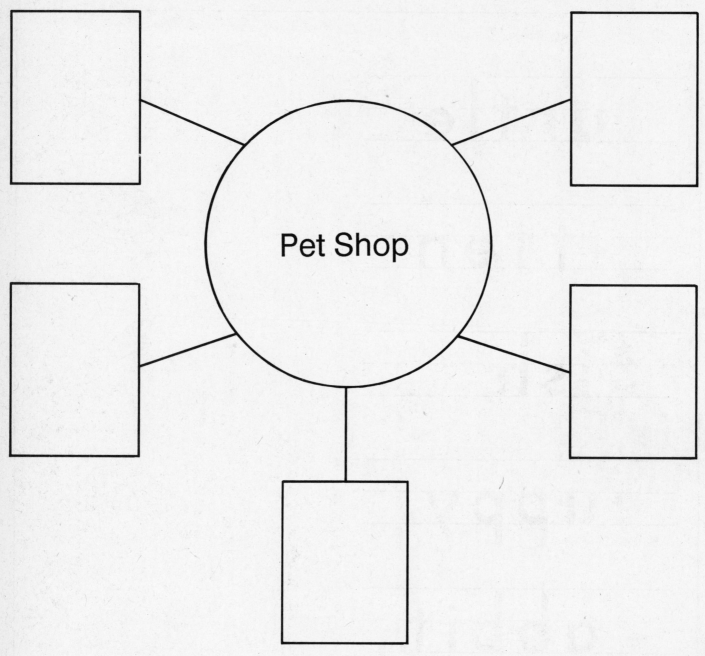

Pet Shop

 carrot

 fish

 kitten

 puppy

 rabbit

 turtle

Name _____

# Pencil Play

Direct students as they:
1. Color and cut out the animals along the dotted lines.
2. Punch holes at small circles.
3. Picture facing up, slide pencil through top hole and then, from the back, through the bottom hole to decorate the pencil.

fold

fold

fold

fold

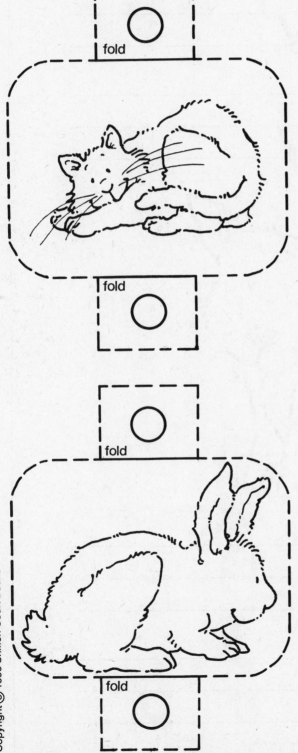

fold

fold

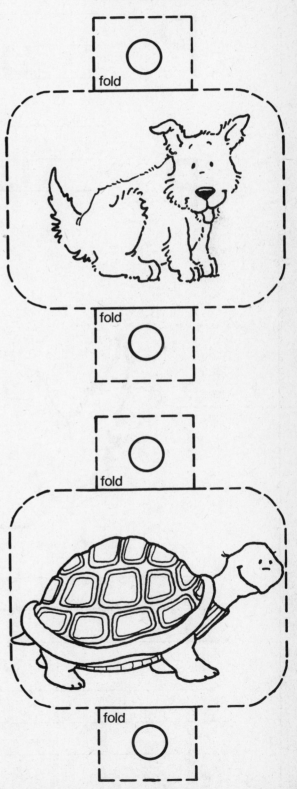

fold

fold

Name _____

Have students trace the beginning
letter in the words at the top of the
page; color the picture; then trace
the letters in the rows below.

P  Puppy

P  puppy

P P P P P P

p p p p p p

Copyright © 1990 Sniffen Court Books

# Name _____

# Name _____

# Pet Bookmarks

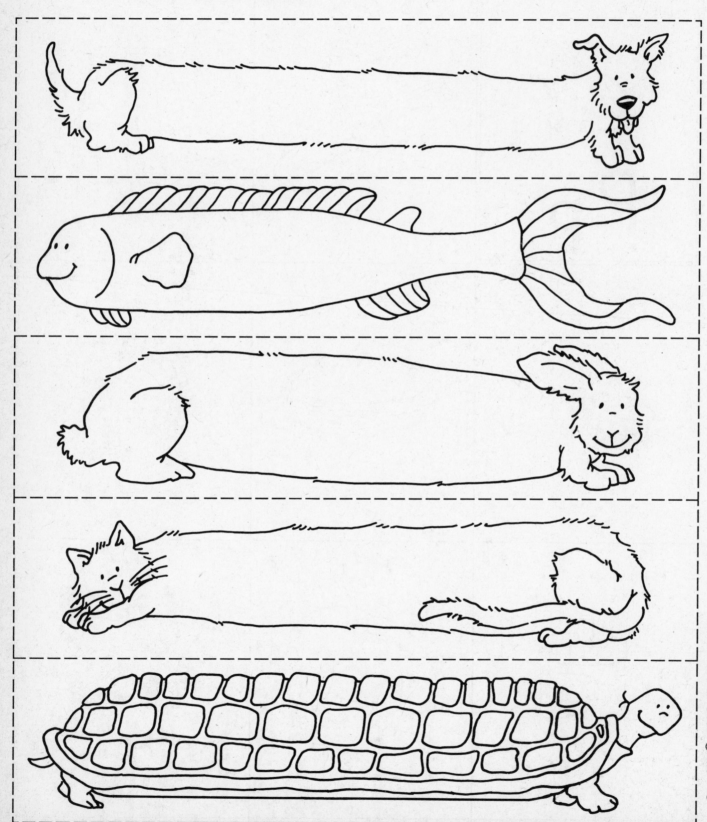

# Name _____

Have students color the pictures, cut them out along the dotted lines, and paste them into their pictionaries in the correct location.

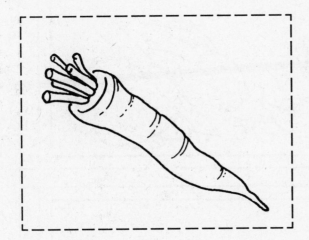

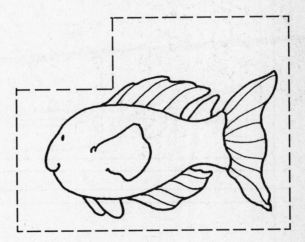

147

_____
Name

## can read these words:

carrot          fish          kitten

puppy          rabbit          turtle

Teacher                                        Date
_____

# UNIT 14: Valentine's Day

**pages 150-159**

## Teacher Notes

**Unit Word List:**

| | |
|---|---|
| crayon | heart |
| paper | paste |
| scissors | valentine |

**Unit Letter:** *Vv*

### Page 150  Building Prior Knowledge

Use the theme picture to develop concepts related to Valentine's Day. The following questions can be used to stimulate language development:

> What is the girl in the picture doing?
>
> What holiday do you think she is getting ready for?
>
> What is she using to make the valentines?
>
> Have you ever made valentines?
>
> What did you make them with?
>
> Who did you send them to?

If students are learning letter-sound relationships, have them pick out all the items in the illustration that start the same as *valentine*: vest, vase, violin, volcano.

### Answers for Activity Pages

**Page 151**  Students should draw a line from each word to the matching picture.

**Page 152**  Students should trace the first letter in each word and draw a circle around the matching picture.

**Page 153**  Students should cut out the scissors, paste, heart, paper, crayon, and paste them around the valentine.

### Page 154  Valentine Hat

Detail of assembly:

### Page 155
Students should trace the first letter in the words at the top of the page, color the picture, and then trace the capital and lower-case *Vv*'s on the lines.

### Page 156
Students should trace the *v* in the box under the valentine and write *v* under violin, vase, vest, and van.

### Page 157  Make a Valentine

Detail of assembly:

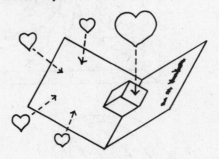

## Additional Unit Activities

### Books

The following books related to Valentine's Day might be read to the students during the completion of this unit:

*The Valentine Party* by Pamela Bianco, New York, J.B. Lippincott, 1955

*Four Valentines in a Rain Storm* by Felicia Bond, New York, Thomas Y. Crowell, 1983

*Little Love Story* by Fernando Krahn, New York, J.B. Lippincott, 1977

Name _____

# Valentine's Day

After discussing the picture, have students circle all the things they would use to make a valentine (crayon, scissors, paper, paste). Then have them put an X on the heart and color the valentine red.

Name _____

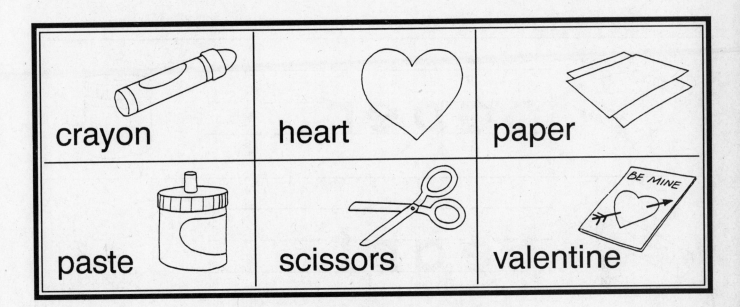

crayon   heart   paper

paste   scissors   valentine

In the boxes below, have students draw a line from each word to the correct picture.

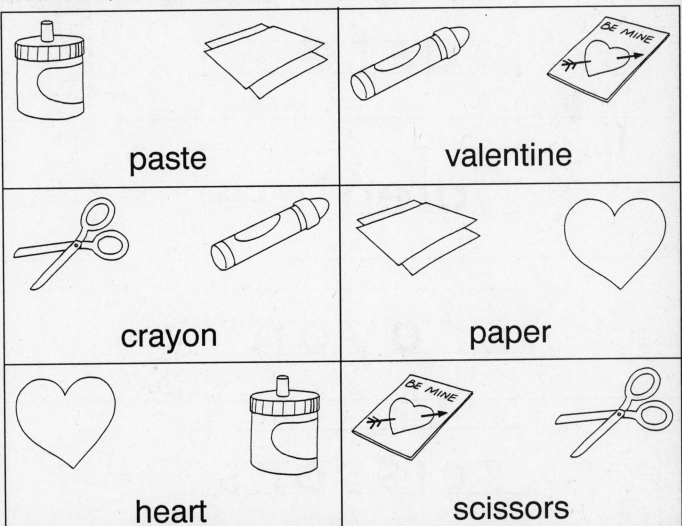

paste   valentine

crayon   paper

heart   scissors

# Name _____

Have students trace the first letter of the word in each box and circle the picture that matches the word.

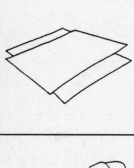 paper

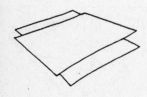 heart

 paste

 valentine

 crayon

 scissors

# Name _____

Have students cut out the boxes at the bottom of the page and paste those objects you might use in making valentines in the empty spaces.

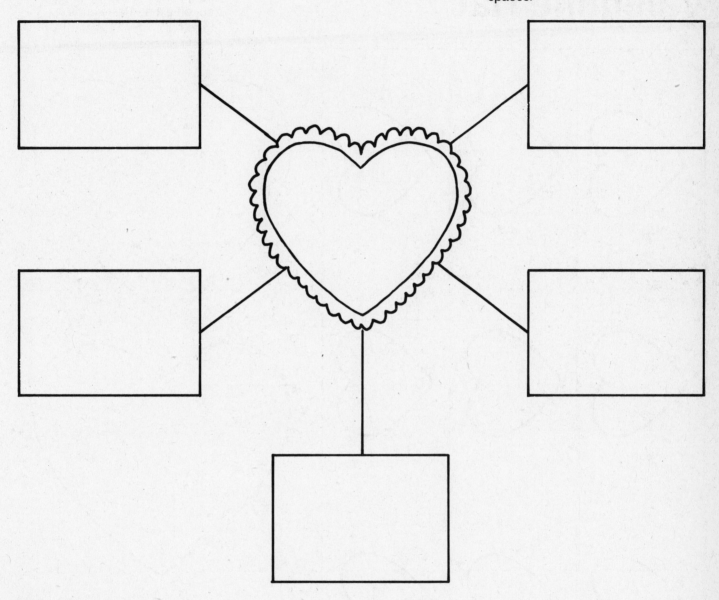

| scissors | heart | paper | crayon |
| paste | radio | ice | sled |

Name _____

# Valentine Hat

Direct students as they:
1. Color and cut out the hearts and hat bands along the dotted lines.
2. Paste hat bands end to end.
3. Fit hat band around head and cut off extra. Paste ends together.
4. Paste on hearts as desired.

Name _____

Have students trace the beginning
letter in the words at the top of the
page;  color the picture; then trace
the letters in the rows below.

V  Valentine

v  valentine

V V V V V V

V V V V V V

Name _____

Have students trace the *v* below the valentine and then write *v* in each box that has a picture of something whose name starts like *valentine*.

BE MINE

v

Name _____

# Make a Valentine

Direct students as they:
1. Color the hearts and the card. Cut them out along the dotted lines.
2. Fold card in half along the solid line and cut the pop-up along the dotted lines.
3. Push pop-up to inside of card. Paste largest heart to pop-up where noted. Paste smaller hearts to card as desired.

*Be my Valentine*

fold

paste | fold

# Name _____

Have students color the pictures, cut them out along the dotted lines, and paste them into their pictionaries in the correct location.

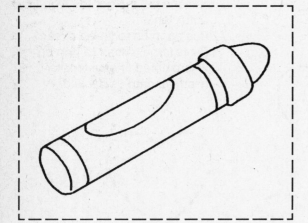

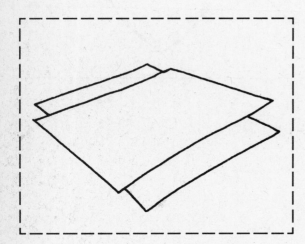

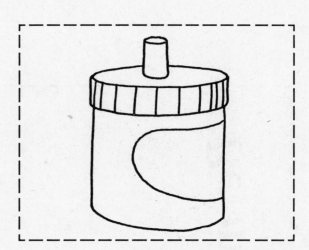

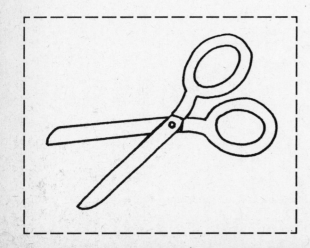

_____
Name

## can read these words:

crayon          heart          paper
paste           scissors       valentine

_____
Teacher                                    Date

## Teacher Notes

### Unit Word List:                    Unit Letter: *Ee*

clown      drum

elephant   horn

tiger      wagon

### Page 161 Building Prior Knowledge

Use the theme picture to develop concepts related to the circus. The following questions can be used to stimulate language development:

What is happening in this picture?

What do we call this kind of entertainment?

Have you ever been to a circus?

Tell us about a circus you have seen?

What is your favorite circus act?

### Answers for Activity Pages

**Page 162** Students should cut out the pictures at the bottom of the page and paste them in the box with the matching words.

**Page 163** Students should trace the first letter in each word and draw a line to the matching picture.

**Page 164** Students should paste *clown, elephant, drum, horn* in the circus tent.

### Page 165 Tiger Tails

Additional materials: paper fasteners

Duplication of this page onto construction or other sturdy paper is recommended.

Detail of assembly:

**Page 166** Students should trace the first letter in the words at the top of the page, color the picture, and then trace the capital and lower-case *Ee*'s on the lines.

**Page 167** Students should color capital *E*'s red and lower-case *e*'s blue.

### Page 168 Pop-up Book

Detail of assembly:

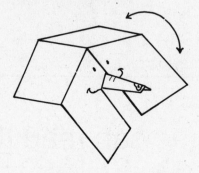 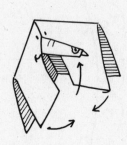

1. Cut out book along dotted lines and color the pictures.
2. Fold along the vertical fold and cut along dotted lines to create the elephant's trunk.
3. Fold along the trunk fold and then unfold the book.
4. Fold along the horizontal fold to create book cover.
5. Push pop-up to the inside of the book and reverse the vertical and trunk folds as necessary to complete the pop-up book.

After the students have assembled their books, let them make up an elephant story and tell it to the class.

## Additional Unit Activities

### Books

The following books related to the circus might be read to the students during the completion of this unit:

*Busy Day* by Betsy and Giulio Maestro, Crown Publishers, Inc., 1978

*Horton Hatches the Egg* by Dr. Seuss, New York, Random House, 1940

*Circus Baby* by Maud and Miska Petersham, New York, Macmillan, 1950

*The Clown's Smile* by Mike Thaler, New York, Harper & Row, 1986

*Brian Wildsmith's Circus* by Brian Wildsmith, New York, Franklin Watts, 1970

# Name _____

# Circus Time

After discussing the picture, have students color: the drum red; the tiger orange; the wagon green. Then have them circle the horn, put an *X* on the clown, and draw a line under the elephant.

# Name _____

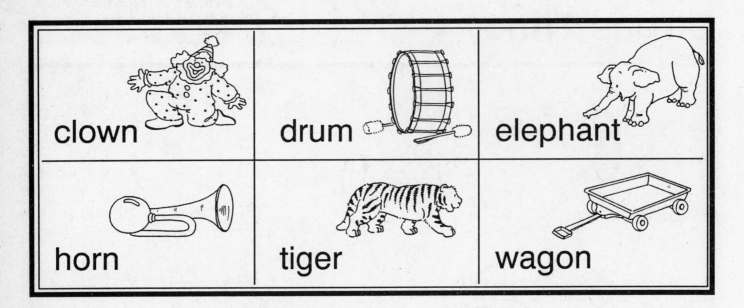

| | | |
|---|---|---|
| clown | drum | elephant |
| horn | tiger | wagon |

Have students cut out the pictures below and paste them above the correct words.

| | | |
|---|---|---|
| elephant | tiger | horn |
| clown | wagon | drum |

   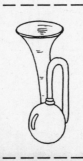  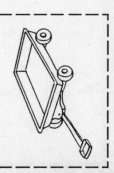

Name _____

Have students trace the first letter of the words and draw a line from each word to the matching picture.

drum

tiger

wagon

horn

elephant

clown

Name _____

Have students cut out the boxes at the bottom of the page and paste the circus words in the spaces in the circus tent.

| sled | clown | elephant |
| bed | drum | horn |

Name _____

# Tiger Tails

Direct students as they:
1. Color the tiger and tail.
2. Cut out the tiger and tail along the dotted lines.
3. Insert a paper fastener through the X on the tiger's back and then through the X on the tail to complete the tiger.

**Name** _____

Have students trace the beginning letter in the words at the top of the page; color the picture; then trace the letters in the rows below.

E   Elephant

e   elephant

E E E E E E

e e e e e e

Name _____

Have students color the capital *E*'s red and lower case *e*'s blue.

# Name _____

# Pop-up Book

Help students to create a pop-up book. See illustrated directions in the Unit 15 Teacher Notes, page 160.

fold

fold

fold

Name _____

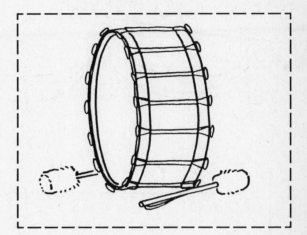

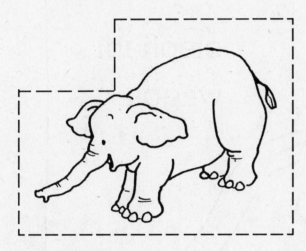

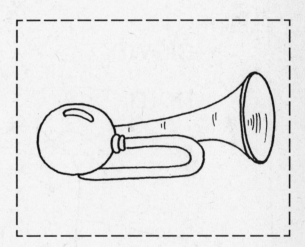

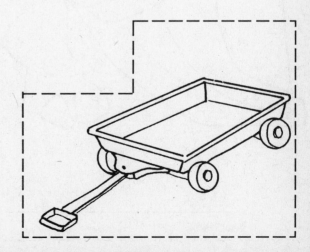

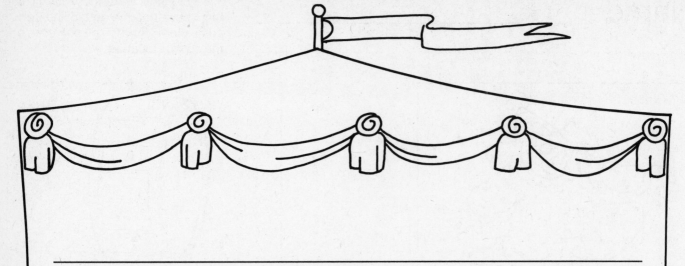

_____
Name

# can read these words:

clown          drum          elephant

horn           tiger          wagon

_____                    _____
Teacher                                                    Date

# UNIT 16: Numbers

## Teacher Notes

### Unit Word List:
one     two

three     four

five      numbers

### Unit Letter: *Oo*

### Page 172 Building Prior Knowledge

Use the theme picture to develop concepts related to the numbers one to five. The following questions can be used to stimulate language development:

> How many lobsters do you see in this picture?
>
> How many turtles?
>
> How many starfish?
>
> How many shells?
>
> How many fish?
>
> Look at the numbers at the bottom of the pages. Can you read the numbers?

Call on a child to read each number. Then have the child point to something in the room that matches the number. (For example: 1 teacher, 2 doors, and so forth)

### Answers for Activity Pages

**Page 173** Students should draw a line from each word to the matching picture.

**Page 174** Students should trace the first letter in each word and draw a line to the matching picture.

**Page 175** Students should paste *one, two, three, four, five* in the boxes with the correct number of items.

### Page 176 Let's Count

Students should paste items to picture as indicated below:

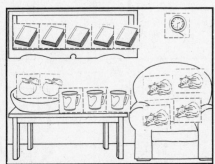

**Page 177** Students should trace the first letter in the words at the top of the page, color the picture, and then trace the capital and lower-case *Oo*'s on the lines.

**Page 178** Students should circle the *Oo*'s in the soup as indicated below:

### Page 179 Number Wheel

Additional materials: paper fasteners

Detail of assembly:

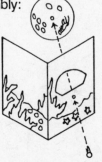

Push scissors through middle of the dotted area and then cut to dotted lines to create a window.

## Additional Unit Activities

### Books

The following books related to numbers might be read to the students during the completion of this unit:

> *Five Little Monkeys Jumping on the Bed* by Eileen Christelow, Boston, Clarion Books, 1989
>
> *The Chicken Book* by Garth Williams, New York, Delacorte Press, 1970
>
> *One Was Johnny* by Maurice Sendak, New York, Harper & Row, 1962
>
> *The Rooster Who Set Off to See the World* by Eric Carle, New York, Franklin Watts, 1972

Name _____

# Numbers

After discussing the picture, have students color the objects as follows: one lobster red; two turtles green; three starfish brown; four shells blue; five fish yellow.

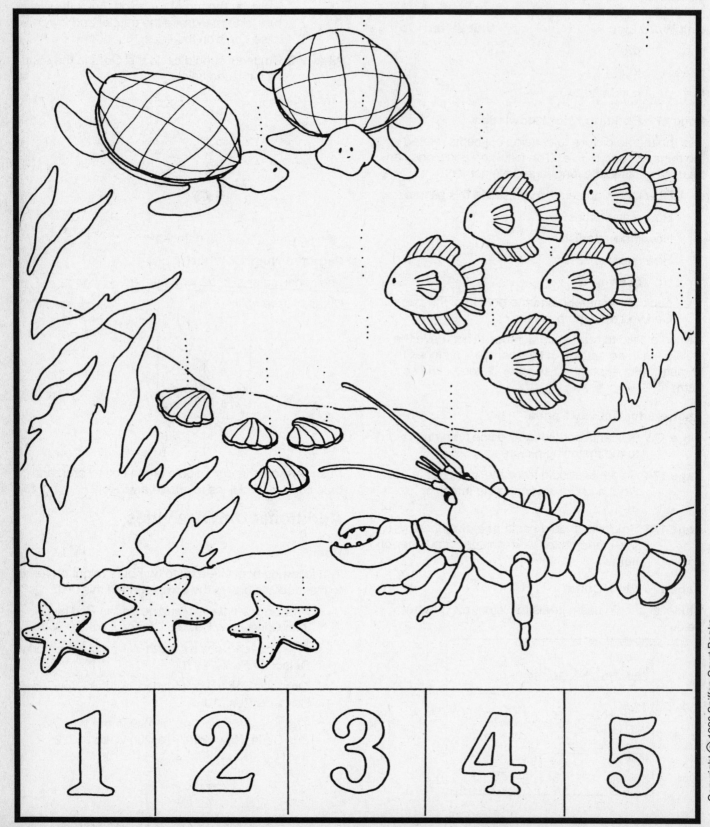

1  2  3  4  5

# Name _____

Have students identify each picture and word in the Word Bank.

| five  5 | four  4 | numbers  2¹⁴³₃₅ |
| one  1 | three  3 | two  2 |

In the boxes below, have students draw a line from each word to the correct picture.

| 4        3 | 2        1 |
|------------|------------|
| four | one |
| 2¹⁴³₃₅        5 | 3        2¹⁴³₃₅ |
| numbers | three |
| 4        2 | 1        5 |
| two | five |

Copyright © 1990 Sniffen Court Books

# Name _____

numbers

two

five

three

one

four

2

3

$2^{14}_{3}{}^{43}_{5}$

4

1

5

# Name _____

## Numbers

| one | drum | two |
|-----|------|-----|
| five | four | three |

Copyright © 1990 Sniffen Court Books

# Name _____

# Let's Count

Direct students as they:
1. Color and cut out the pictures along the dotted lines.
2. Paste one clock on the wall, two apples in the bowl, three cups on the table, four kittens on the chair, and five books on the shelves.

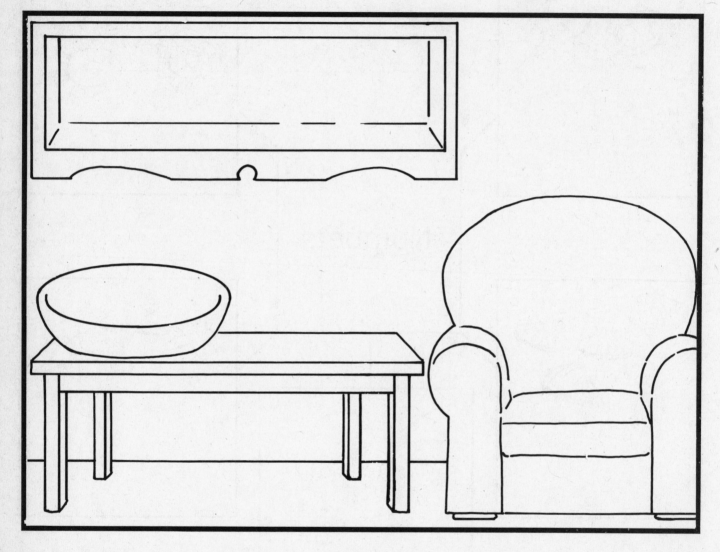

Name _____

Have students trace the beginning letter in the words at the top of the page; color the picture; then trace the letters in the rows below.

O o    One    one

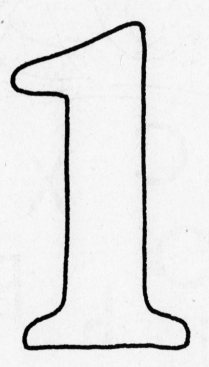

Name _____

Name _____

# Number Wheel

Direct students as they:
1. Color the pictures and cut them out along the dotted lines.
2. Cut out window in card along dotted lines.
3. Push a paper fastener through the circle on the card and then through the circle on the wheel.
4. Fold card along vertical fold. When wheel is turned, pictures in window will change.

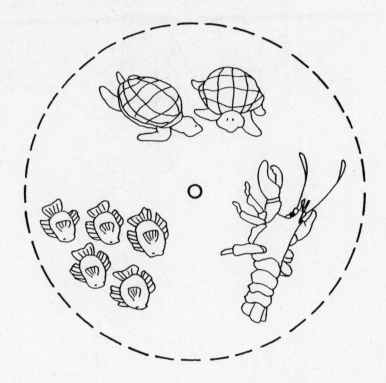

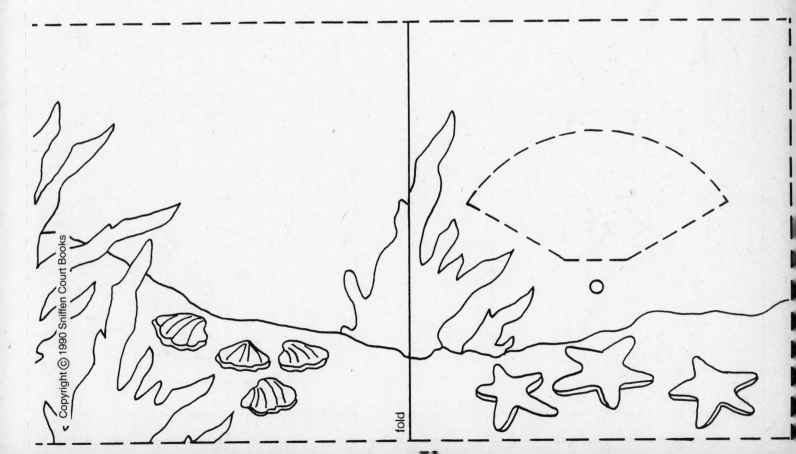

fold

# Name _____

Have students color the pictures, cut them out along the dotted lines, and paste them into their pictionaries in the correct location.

5

4

2 1 4 3 3 5

1

3

2

# can read these words:

| one | two | three |
|-----|-----|-------|
| four | five | numbers |

Teacher                                                                Date

## Teacher Notes

**Unit Word List:**          **Unit Letter:** *Nn*

bird          butterfly

flower          kite

nest          rainbow

### Page 183 Building Prior Knowledge

Use the theme picture to develop concepts related to spring. The following questions can be used to stimulate language development:

> What season of the year does this picture show?
>
> What are the people doing?
>
> Why is spring a good time for kites?
>
> Is this how spring looks where we live?
>
> What do you look forward to in spring?

If students are learning letter-sound relationships, have them pick out all the items in the illustration that start the same as *nest*: newspaper, nurse, nuts.

### Answers for Activity Pages:

**Page 184** Students should cut out the words at the bottom of the page and paste them in the box with the matching picture.

**Page 185** Students should trace the first letter in each word and draw a circle around the matching picture.

**Page 186** Students should paste the bird, butterfly, flower, kite, nest, and rainbow around *Spring*.

### Page 187 Flower Time

Detail of assembly:

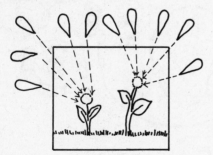

**Page 188** Students should trace the first letter in the words at the top of the page, color the picture, and then trace the capital and lower-case *Nn*'s on the lines.

**Page 189** Students should draw a circle around numbers, nurse, nuts, and newspaper.

### Page 190 Make a Kite

Additional materials: 7 feet of string per student, crepe paper or plastic bags

Detailed assembly instructions and diagrams can be found on page 190.

## Additional Unit Activities

### Books

The following books related to spring might be read to the students during the completion of this unit:

> *Katy in the Morning* by Crescent Dragonwagon, New York, Harper & Row, 1983
>
> *The Sugar Snow Spring* by Lillian Hoban, New York, Harper & Row, 1973
>
> *Will Spring Be Early or Will Spring Be Late?* by Crockett Johnson, New York, Thomas Y. Crowell, 1959
>
> *The Happy Day* by Ruth Kraus, New York, Harper & Row, 1949

### Poem

**Catkin**

I have a little pussy,
    And her coat is silver grey;
She lives in a great meadow
    And she never runs away.
She always is a pussy,
    She'll never be a cat
Because--she's a pussy willow!
    Now what do you think of that!

*Unknown*

# Name _____

# Spring

After discussing the picture, have
students color: the flowers yellow;
the kite red; the nest brown; the
rainbow in a variety of colors of their
choice. Then have them circle the
bird and draw a line under the
butterfly.

# Name _____

Have students identify each picture
and word in the Word Bank.

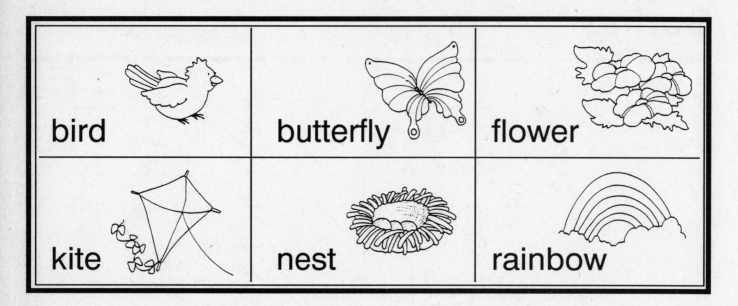

| | | |
|---|---|---|
| bird | butterfly | flower |
| kite | nest | rainbow |

Have students cut out the words at the bottom of the page and paste them below the correct pictures.

| kite | flower | nest |
|---|---|---|
| rainbow | bird | butterfly |

Name _____

Have students trace the first letter of the word in each box and circle the picture that matches the word.

 nest

 flower

 rainbow

 butterfly

 bird

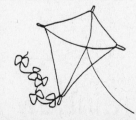 kite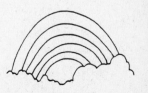

Copyright © 1990 Sniffen Court Books

Name _____

Have students cut out the boxes at the bottom of the page and paste around *Spring* those that show things you see in the spring.

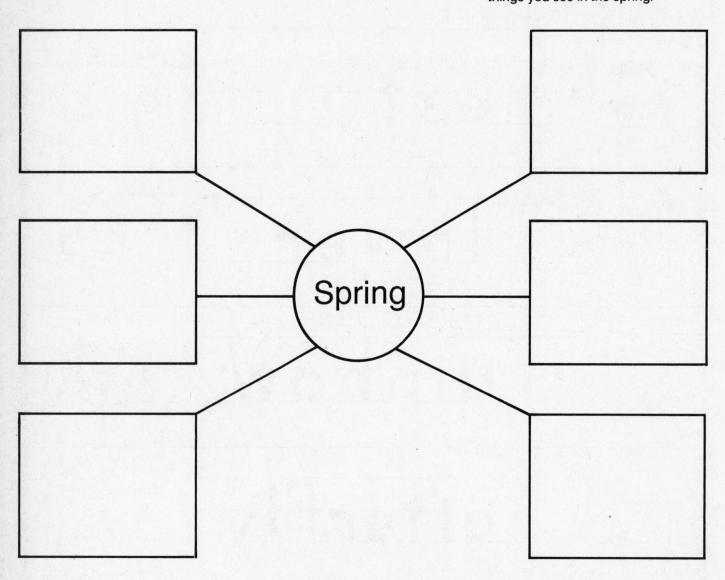

Spring

bird  snowman  butterfly  flower

sled  kite  nest  rainbow

Name _____

# Flower Time

Direct students as they:
1. Color and cut out the flower petals along the dotted lines.
2. Paste petals in place around the flower centers to complete flowers.

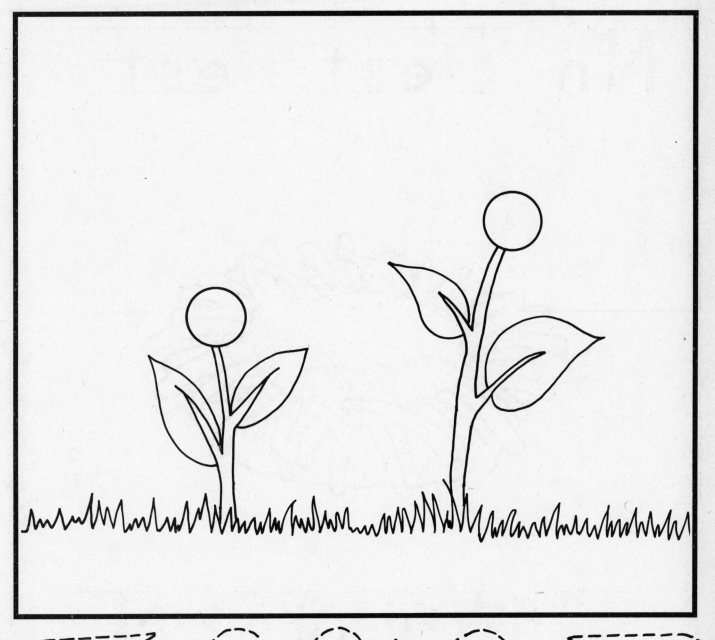

Name _____

Have students trace the beginning letter in the words at the top of the page; color the picture; then trace the letters in the rows below.

N n  Nest nest

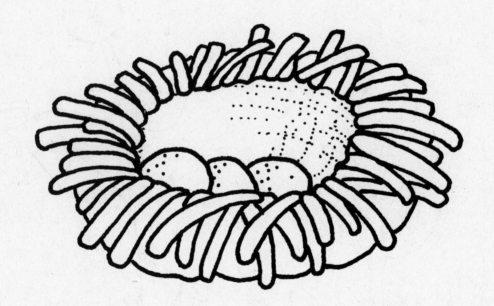

N N N N N N

n n n n n n

Name _____

Have students circle the object that begin with the same sound as the objects at the top of the page.

# N n

# Name _____ O

# Make a Kite

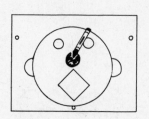

Direct students as they:

1. Cut out diamond shape along the dotted lines. Punch holes at circles. Reinforce with paper reinforcements or tape.
2. Color the reverse side of this paper.

old

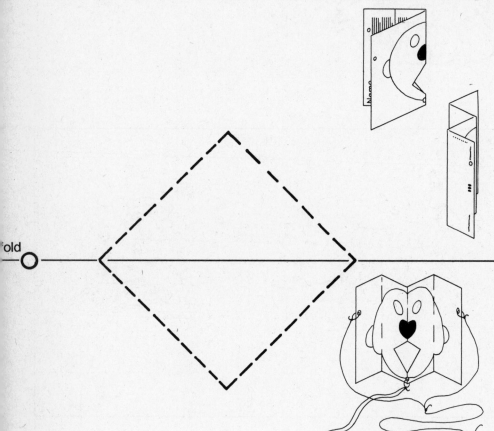

3. Accordian fold along lines: fold in half along center line, colored design to the outside; then fold sides down to center along fold lines, colored design to the inside.
4. Attach each end of an 18-inch string at the side holes to form the bridle. Attach a 4-foot string to the center of the bridle.

5. Attach a narrow tail (1 inch wide) about 3 feet long of crepe paper or plastic bag cut into strips to the third hole.
6. To fly kite, keep fold and colored side facing into the wind.

old

fold

Name _____

Have students color the pictures, cut them out along the dotted lines, and paste them into their pictionaries in the correct location.

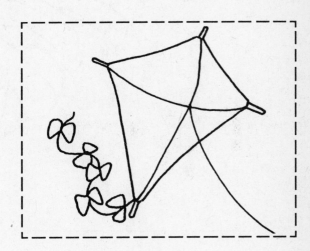

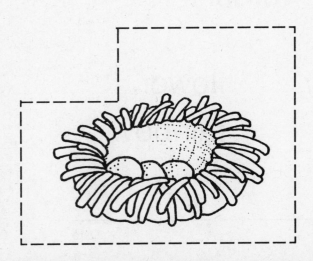

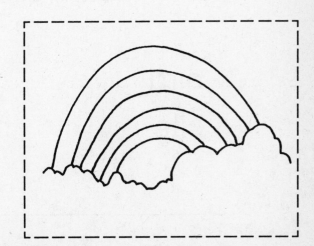

_____

Name

## can read these words:

bird         butterfly       flower

kite          nest           rainbow

_____

Teacher                                 Date

## Teacher Notes

**Unit Word List:**        **Unit Letter:** *G g*

barn    chicken
cow     goat
horse   pig

### Page 194 Building Prior Knowledge

Use the theme picture to develop concepts related to farming. The following questions can be used to stimulate language development:

Where are the children in this picture?

What are they doing?

What animals do you see?

Have you ever visited a real farm?

Where do the animals live on this farm?

If students are learning letter-sound relationships, have them pick out all the items in the illustration that start the same as *goat*: gate, girl, geese.

### Answers for Activity Pages

**Page 195** Students should cut out the pictures at the bottom of the page and paste them in the box with the matching words.

**Page 196** Students should trace the first letter in each word and draw a line to the matching picture.

**Page 197** Students should paste the cow, horse, pig, goat, and chicken in the barn.

### Page 198 Finger Puppets

Duplication of this page onto construction or other sturdy paper is recommended.

Detail of assembly:

**Page 199** Students should trace the first letter in the words at the top of the page, color the picture, and then trace the capital and lower-case *Gg*'s on the lines.

**Page 200** Students should draw a line from *Gg* to the goat, goose, gate, and girl.

### Page 201 A Farm Game

Duplication of this page onto construction or other sturdy paper is recommended.

## Additional Unit Activities

### Books

The following books related to the farm might be read to the students during the completion of the farm unit:

*The Chicken Book* by Garth Williams, New York: Thomas Y. Crowell, 1946

*Rosie's Walk* by Pat Hutchins, New York: Macmillan, 1968

*Early Morning in the Barn* by Nancy Tafaui, New York: Viking, Puffin Books, 1986

### Poems

#### The Cow

The friendly cow all red and white,
    I love with all my heart;
She gives me cream with all her might,
    To eat with apple tart.

She wanders lowing here and there,
    And yet she cannot stray,
All in the pleasant open air,
    The pleasant light of day;

And blown by all the winds that pass
    And wet with all the showers,
She walks among the meadow grass,
    And eats the meadow flowers.

*Robert Louis Stevenson*

#### There Lived a Little Man

Once there lived a little man
Where a little river ran,
And he had a little farm and a little dairy O!
    And he had a little plough,
    And a little dappled cow,
Which he often called his pretty little fairy O!

    And his dog he called Fidele,
    For he loved his master well,
And he had a little pony for his pleasure O!
    In a sty, not very big,
    He'd a frisky little pig
Which he often called his little piggy treasure O!

*Traditional*

Name _____

# On the Farm

After discussing the picture, have students color the barn red. Then have them circle the following animals as you name them: chicken, cow, goat, horse, pig.

# Name _____

Have students cut out the pictures below and paste them above the correct words.

| | | |
|---|---|---|
| chicken | horse | goat |
| barn | cow | pig |

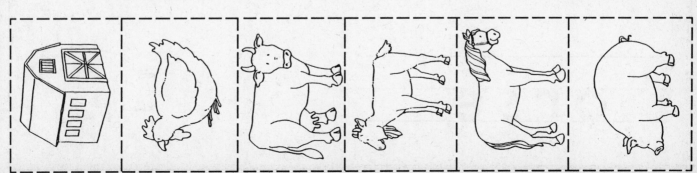

Name _____

Have students trace the first letter of the words and draw a line from each word to the matching picture.

cow

chicken

barn

pig

goat

horse

Name _____

tiger | cow | horse | pig | goat | chicken

Name _____

# Finger Puppets

Direct students as they:
1. Color and cut out the finger puppets along the dotted lines.
2. Wrap the tabs around a finger to test the fit. Cut off excess paper.
3. Paste the tabs together to complete puppets.

paste

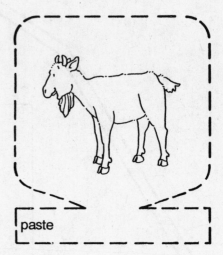

paste

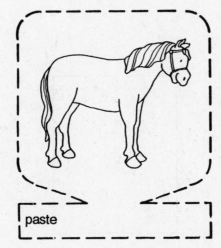

paste

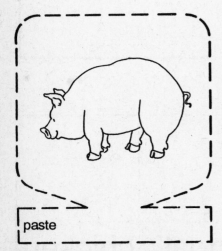

paste

paste

# Name _____

Have students trace the beginning letter in the words at the top of the page; color the picture; then trace the letters in the rows below.

Gg Goat goat

G G G G G G

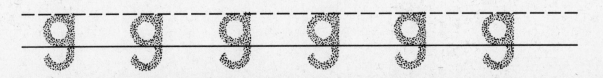

g g g g g g

**Name** _____

# G g

Name _____

# A Farm Game

Direct students to color the game board and animal game pieces. Then cut out the game pieces along the dotted lines and fold in half to stand up.
To play the game:
1. Choose a game piece. Put three pennies in a cup.
2. In turn, each player spills the pennies out of the cup and moves the number of "heads" that come up. The first player to the barn wins.

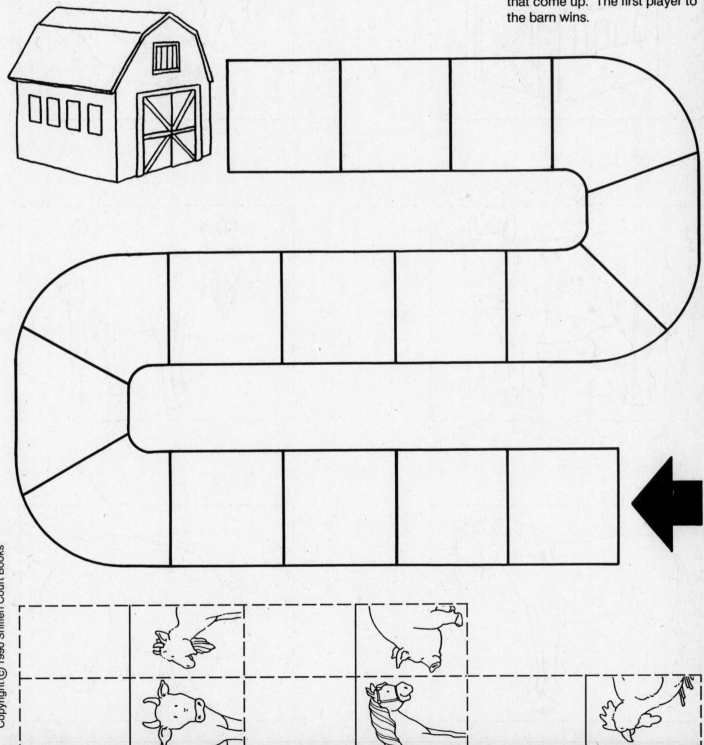

# Name _____

Have students color the pictures, cut them out along the dotted lines, and paste them into their pictionaries in the correct location.

_____
Name

## can read these words:

barn          chicken          cow
goat          horse            pig

_____
Teacher                                    Date

## Teacher Notes

### Unit Word List:

Unit Letter: *A a*

| | |
|---|---|
| ant | apple |
| banana | basket |
| pie | tree |

### Page 205 Building Prior Knowledge

Use the theme picture to develop concepts related to picnics. The following questions can be used to stimulate language development:

What is happening in the picture?

Have you ever had a picnic?

Where did you go?

What are the people in the picture having to eat at their picnic?

What kind of picnic food do you like?

Why do ants like picnics?

### Answers for Activity Pages

**Page 206** Students should draw a line from each word to the matching picture.

**Page 207** Students should trace the first letter in each word and draw a line to the matching picture.

**Page 208** Students should paste the basket, pie, apple, ant, banana on the blanket.

### Page 209 Picnic Maze

Students should thread through the maze as indicated below:

**Page 210** Students should trace the first letter in the words at the top of the page, color the picture, and then trace the capital and lower-case *Aa* 's on the lines.

**Page 211** Students should color the ants carrying the capital *A's* red and the lower-case *a's* brown.

### Page 212 Basket Weaving

Detail of assembly:

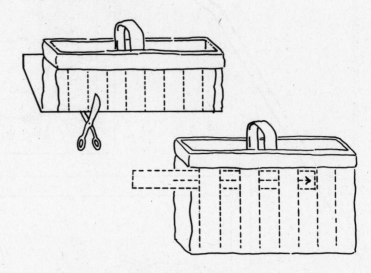

Fold paper in half perpendicular to dotted lines and then cut across fold along dotted lines to make slits.

## Additional Unit Activities

### Books

The following books related to picnics and parks might be read to the students during the completion of this unit:

*A Tree Is Nice* by Janice Udry, New York: Harper & Row, 1956

*Jenny's Birthday Book* by Esther Averill, New York: Harper & Row, 1954

*Picnic* by Emily Arnold McCully, New York: Harper & Row, 1984

*Two Bad Ants* by Chris Van Allsburg, Boston: Houghton Mifflin, 1989

# Name _____

# A Picnic

After discussing the picture, have students color: the apples red; the banana yellow; the pie brown. Then have them put an X on the basket, circle the ants and draw a line under the tree.

# Name _____

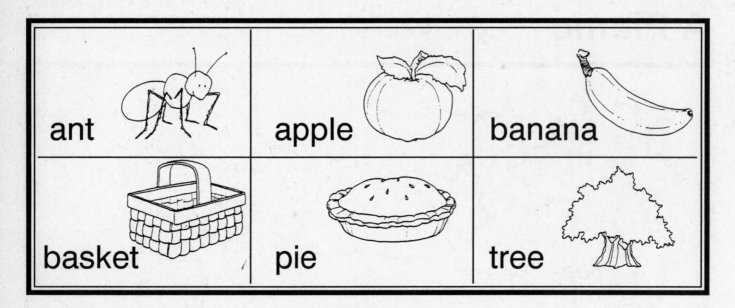

ant     apple     banana

basket     pie     tree

In the boxes below, have students draw a line from each word to the correct picture.

pie     banana

tree     ant

apple     basket

# Name _____

Have students trace the first letter of the words and then draw a line from each word to the matching picture.

ant

basket

apple

banana

tree

pie

# Name _____

Have students cut out the boxes at the bottom of the page and paste those on the blanket that might be found on a picnic.

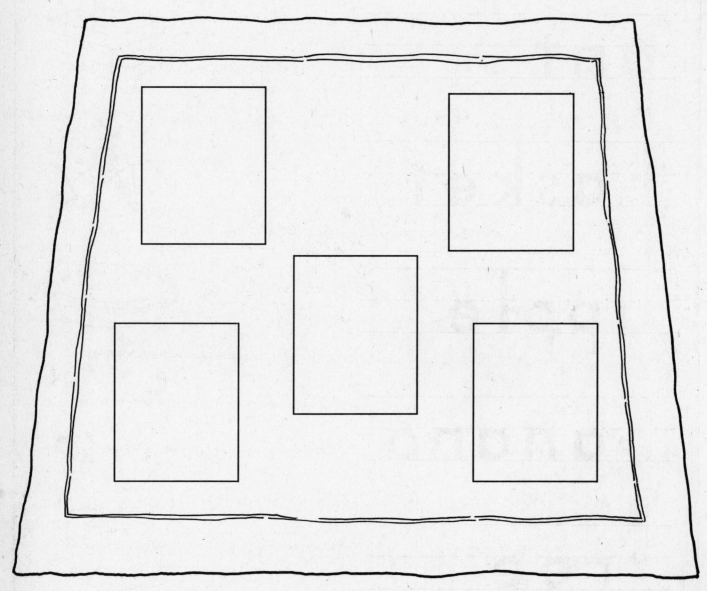

basket | pie | apple | door | ant | banana

Name _____

Direct students to complete the maze, helping the ant to find the picnic basket.

# Picnic Maze

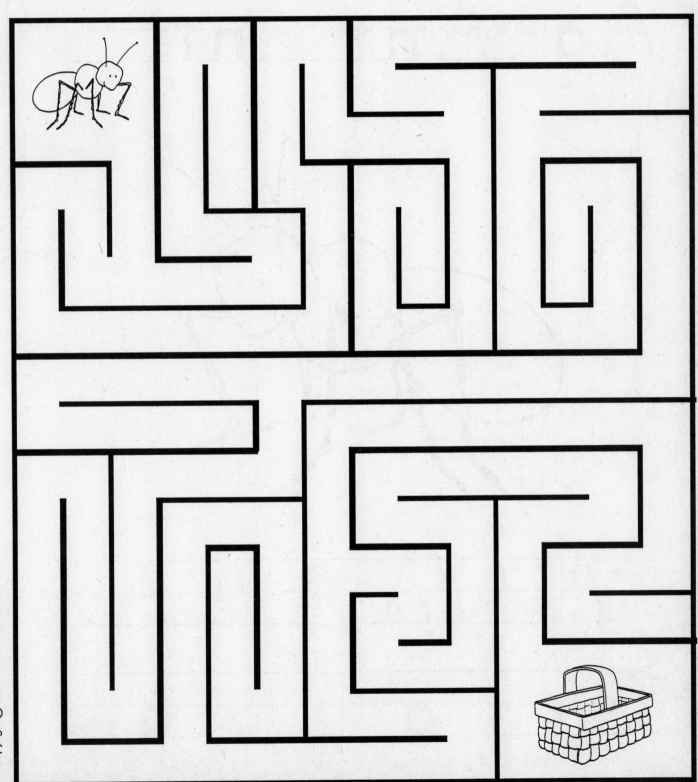

Name _____

Have students trace the beginning letter in the words at the top of the page; color the picture; then trace the letters in the rows below.

# A a   Ant ant

A A A A A A

a a a a a a

# Name _____

Have children color all the ants carrying capital *A*'s red and lower case *a*'s brown.

Name _____

# Basket Weaving

Direct students as they:
1. Color the basket and cut the slits along the dotted lines.
2. Color the strips at the bottom and cut them out along the dotted lines.
3. Weave the strips over and under the slits in the basket. Trim strips that are too long.

# Name _____

Have students color the pictures, cut them out along the dotted lines, and paste them into their pictionaries in the correct location.

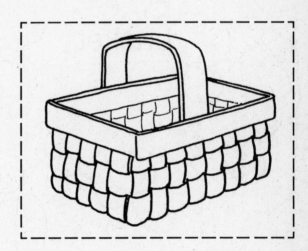

_____
Name

## can read these words:

| | | |
|---|---|---|
| ant | apple | banana |
| basket | pie | tree |

# UNIT 20: Colors

## Teacher Notes

**Unit Word List:**           **Unit Letter:** *Yy*

blue          green

orange        purple

red           yellow

### Page 216 Building Prior Knowledge

Use the theme picture to develop concepts related to colors. The following questions can be used to stimulate language development:

> What kinds of fruits and vegetables do you see on the table?
>
> What color would carrots be?
>
> What color would bananas be?
>
> What fruit might be red?
>
> What fruit might be purple?
>
> What color would the lettuce be?
>
> What color are the blueberries?
>
> What is your favorite fruit?

If students are learning letter-sound relationships, have them pick out all the items in the illustration that start the same as *yellow*: yard, yarn, yo-yo.

### Answers for Activity Pages

**Page 217** Students should cut out the words at the bottom of the page and paste them in the box with the matching picture.

**Page 218** Students should trace the first letter in each word and circle the matching picture.

**Page 219** Students should color each strip the color indicated and paste them on the rainbow.

### Page 220 Color Game

Have students paste the cut-out cards on cardboard or construction paper to make them more durable and less transparent.

**Page 221** Students should trace the first letter in the words at the top of the page, color the picture, and then trace the capital and lowercase *Yy*'s on the lines.

**Page 222** Students should draw a circle around the yarn and yard.

### Page 223 Hidden Picture

Be sure students have colored the picture as indicated by the letter in each space to reveal an orange, grapes, apple, banana.

## Additional Unit Activities

### Books

The following books related to color might be read to the students during the completion of this unit:

> *Color Seems*, by Ilma Haskins, New York: The Vanguard Press, 1973
>
> *Little Blue and Little Yellow* by Leo Lionni, New York: Astor-Honor Press, 1959
>
> *The Animals Who Changed Their Colors* by Pascale Allamand, New York: Lothrop, Lee & Shepard Company, 1979
>
> *If You Take a Paintbrush* by Fulvio Testa, New York: Dial Press, 1982
>
> *The Rainbow-Colored Horse* by Pura Belpré, New York: Frederick Warne & Co., 1978

# Name _____

# Colors

After discussing the picture, have students color: the apples red; the carrots orange; the bananas yellow; the lettuce green; the berries blue; the grapes purple.

# Name _____

| blue | green | orange |
|------|-------|--------|
| purple | red | yellow |

Have students color the circles to match object keys as colored above. Then have them cut out the words at the bottom of the page and paste them below the pictures of the matching color.

| | | |
|--|--|--|
| | | |

| red | orange | yellow |
|-----|--------|--------|
| green | blue | purple |

Name _____

Have students color the circles with object keys as follows: grapes, purple; lettuces, green; bananas, yellow; apples, red; berries, blue; carrots, orange. Then have them trace the first letter of each word and circle the picture that matches the color word.

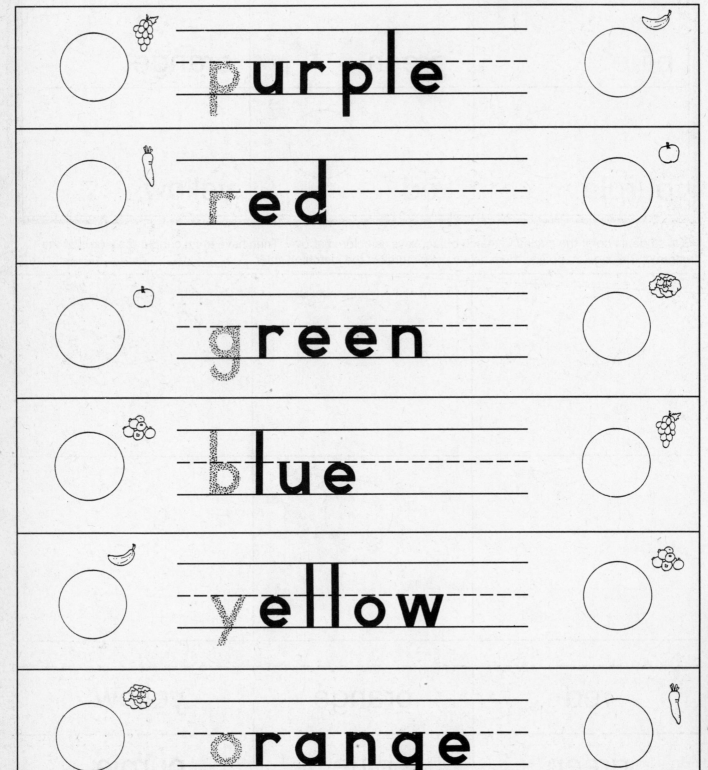

purple

red

green

blue

yellow

orange

Name _____

Have students color the strips at the bottom of the page according to the color words on the strips. Then have them cut out the strips and paste them on the rainbow.

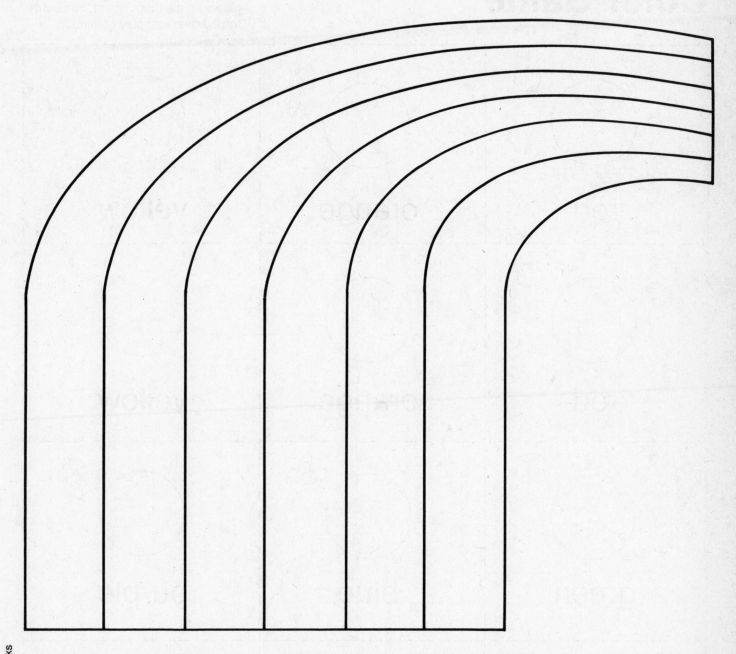

| red | orange |
| yellow | green |
| blue | purple |

# Name _____

# Color Game

Have students color and cut out the cards along the dotted lines.
To play the game, mix and turn cards face down. In turn, each player turns up two cards. If the cards match, the player keeps them. If not, cards are turned over and play continues.

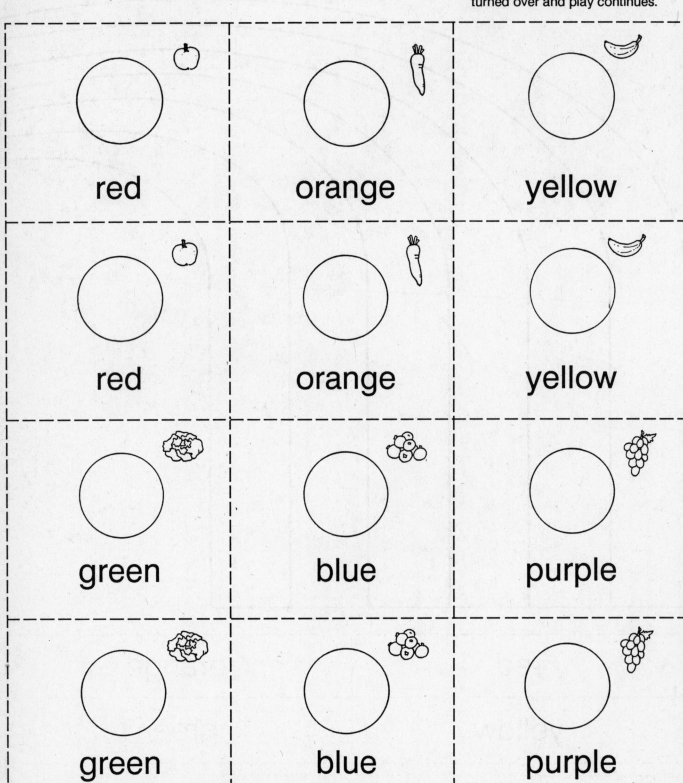

red

orange

yellow

red

orange

yellow

green

blue

purple

green

blue

purple

Name _____

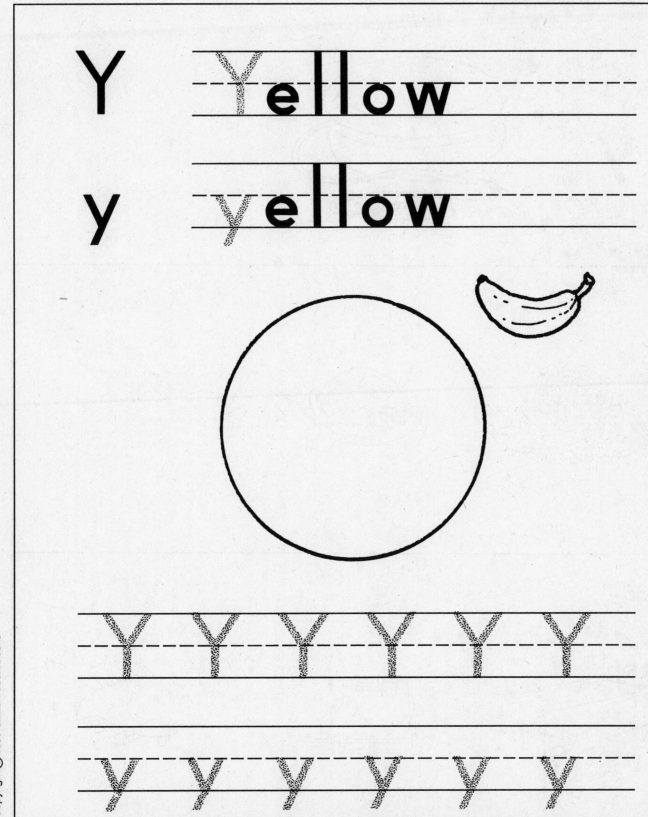

# Name _____

Have students circle the objects that begin with the same sound as the object at the top of the page.

# Y y

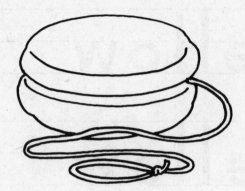

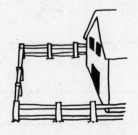

Direct students to colors the spaces as follows: R, red; O, orange; Y, yellow; G, green; B, blue; P, purple.

# Hidden Picture

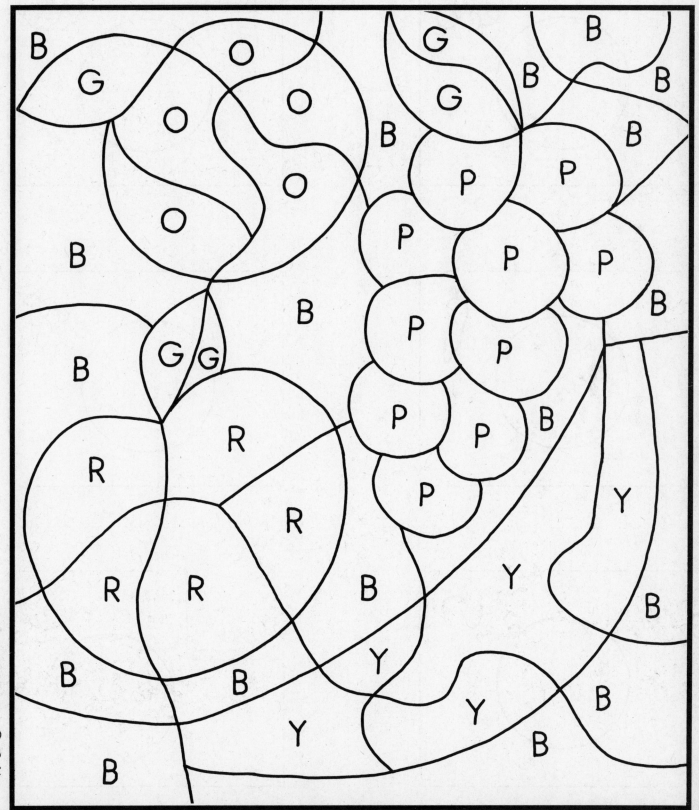

# Name _____

Have students color the pictures, cut them out along the dotted lines, and paste them into their pictionaries in the correct location.

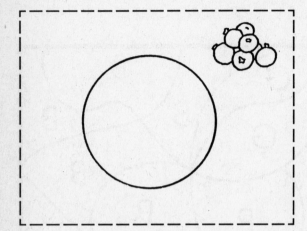

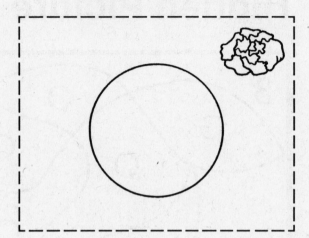

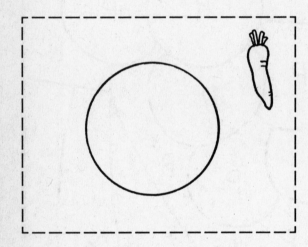

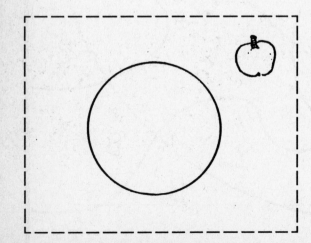

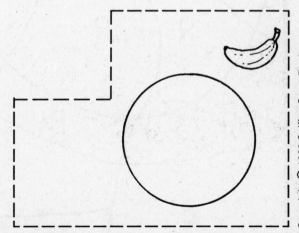

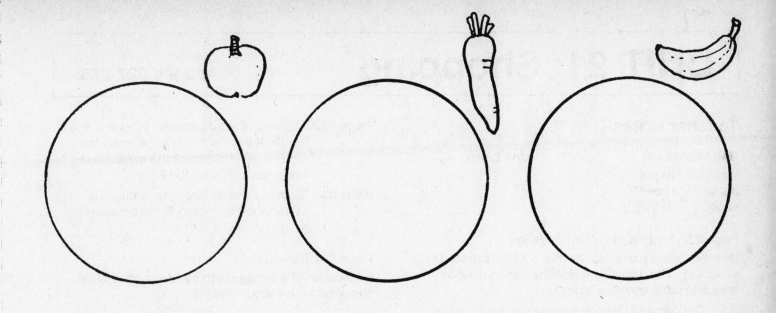

_____
Name

## can read these words:

blue            green           orange
purple          red             yellow

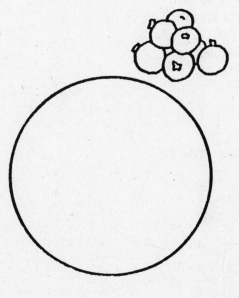

_____
Teacher                                    Date

# UNIT 21: Shopping

## Teacher Notes

**Unit Word List:**                    **Unit Letter:** *J j*

dress          jacket
pants          shoes
socks          T-shirt

### Page 227  Building Prior Knowledge

Use the theme picture to develop concepts related to shopping. The following questions can be used to stimulate language development:

> The people in this picture are shopping. What might they want to buy?
>
> What do you see in the picture that you would want to buy if you could shop with them?
>
> Do you ever go shopping with your family?
>
> What stores do you like to shop in?

If students are learning letter-sound relationships, have them pick out all the items in the illustration that start the same as *jacket*: jeans, jumprope, jacks.

### Answers for Activity Pages

**Page 228**  Students should cut out the pictures at the bottom of the page and paste them in the box with the matching words.

**Page 229**  Students should trace the first letter in each word and draw a line to the matching picture.

**Page 230**  Students should paste *dress, jacket, pants, shoes, socks, T-shirt* in the shopping bags.

### Page 231  Make a Bow Tie

Additional materials: ribbon or yarn
Duplication of this page onto construction or other sturdy paper is recommended.

Detail of assembly:

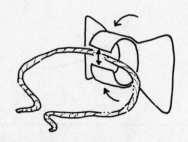

**Page 232**  Students should trace the first letter in the words at the top of the page, color the picture, and then trace the capital and lower-case *Jj* 's on the lines.

**Page 233**  Students should trace the *j* under the jacket and then write *j* in the boxes with jar, jeans, and jump rope.

### Page 234  Paper Dolls

Duplication of this page onto construction or other sturdy paper is recommended.

## Additional Unit Activities

### Books

The following books related to shopping might be read to the students during the completion of this unit:

> *On Market Street* by Arnold Lobel, New York: Greenwillow, 1981
>
> *The Little Old Man Who Could Not Read* by Irma Simonton Black, Niles, Illinois: Albert Whitman, 1968
>
> *I Will Not Go to Market Today* by Harry Allard, New York: Dial, 1979

Copyright © 1990 Sniffen Court Books

**Name** _____

After discussing the picture, have students color the items on display: the socks red; the dress green; the jacket purple; the T-shirt yellow; the pants blue; the shoes brown.

# Shopping

# Name _____

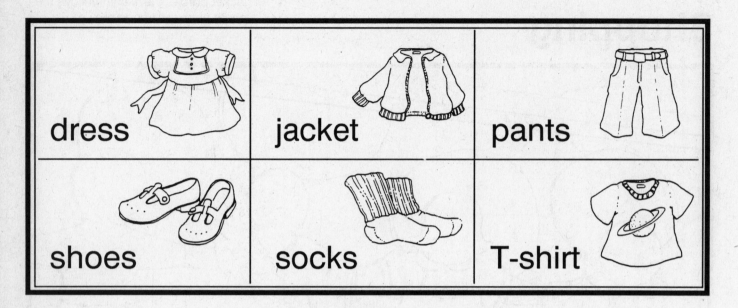

| dress | jacket | pants |
| shoes | socks | T-shirt |

Have students cut out the pictures below and paste them above the correct words.

| pants | jacket | socks |
|---|---|---|
| shoes | T-shirt | dress |

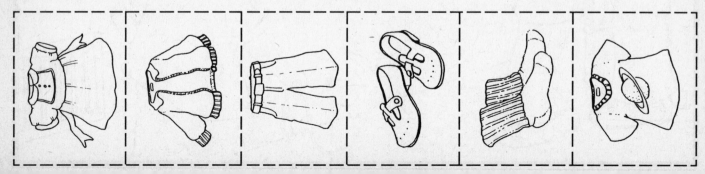

Name _____

rightHave students trace the first letter of
the words and draw a line from each
word to the matching picture.

shoes

pants

T-shirt

jacket

dress

socks

Name _____

Have students cut out the words at the bottom of the page and paste in the shopping bags those that name items that would be found in a clothing store.

| dress | jacket | pants | apple |
| shoes | socks | barn | T-shirt |

Name _____

# Make a Bow Tie

Direct students as they:
1. Color and cut out the bow ties along the dotted lines.
2. Fold tabs to back of tie and paste one tab on top of the other.
3. Cut an 18-inch length of yarn. Slip one end through the loop in the back of the bow tie and use yarn to secure bow tie around neck.

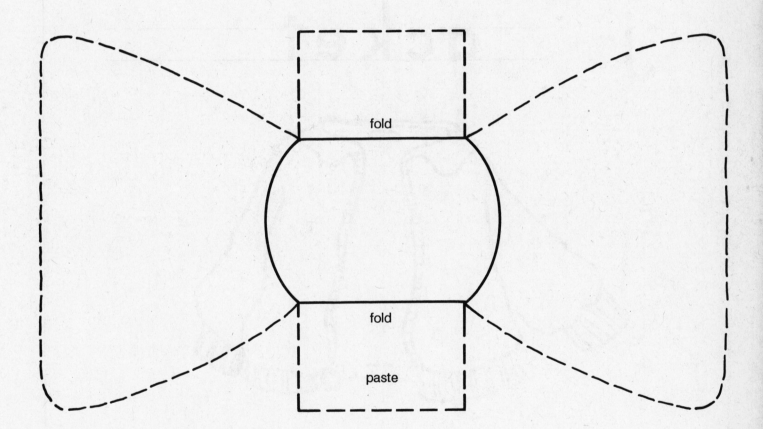

fold

fold

paste

Name _____

J Jacket

J jacket

J J J J J J

j j j j j j

## Teacher Notes

**Unit Word List:**

| | |
|---|---|
| cake | candy |
| cup | hat |
| ice cream | present |

**Unit Letter:** *H h*

### Page 238  Building Prior Knowledge

Use the theme picture to develop concepts related to birthday parties. The following questions can be used to stimulate language development:

> What kind of a party are the people in the picture having?
>
> What are they having to eat?
>
> Have you ever been to a birthday party?
>
> What did you have to eat?
>
> What games did you play?
>
> What might be in the packages that the boy is getting for his birthday?

If students are learning letter-sound relationships, have them pick out all the items in the illustration that start the same as *hat*: heart, horn, hair, house, horse, hands.

### Answers for Activity Pages

**Page 239** Students should draw a line from each word to the matching picture.

**Page 240** Students should trace the first letter in each word and draw a line to the matching picture.

**Page 241** Students should paste *cake, cup, ice cream, candy, hat, present* on the candles.

### Page 242  A Birthday Card

Detail of assembly:

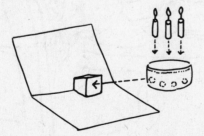

**Page 243** Students should trace the first letter in the words at the top of the page, color the picture, and then trace the capital and lower-case *Hh* 's on the lines.

**Page 244** Students should draw a circle around the heart, horn, house, horse.

### Page 245  Puzzle Picture

Duplication of this page onto construction or other sturdy paper is recommended.

## Additional Unit Activities

### Books

The following books related to birthdays might be read to the students during the completion of this unit:

*The Secret Birthday Message* by Eric Carle, New York: Thomas Y. Crowell, 1972

*The Birthday Tree* by Paul Fleischman, New York: Harper & Row, 1979

*Mary Betty Lizzie McNutt's Birthday* by Felicia Bond, New York: Thomas Y. Crowell, 1983

Name _____

# The Birthday Party

After discussing the picture, have students color: the presents yellow; the hats blue. Then have them put an *X* on the cups and circle the following items as you say them: cake, candy, ice cream.

# Name _____

cake   candy   cup

hat   ice cream   present

In the boxes below, have students draw a line from each word to the correct picture.

cup   hat

present   candy

ice cream   cake

Name _____

Have students trace the first letter of the words and then draw a line from each word to the matching picture.

candy

cake

present

cup

hat

ice cream

Name _____

Have students cut out the words at the bottom of the page and paste on the candles those that name things that might be found at a birthday party.

| cake | x-ray | cup | ice cream |
| bus | candy | hat | present |

**Name** _____

# A Birthday Card

Direct students as they:
1. Color the cake, candles, and card. Cut them out along the dotted lines.
2. Fold card in half along the solid line and cut the pop-up along the dotted lines.
3. Push pop-up to inside of card. Paste cake to pop-up where noted. Paste candles to cake as desired.

*Happy Birthday*

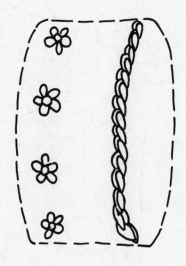

fold

fold

paste

*to you*

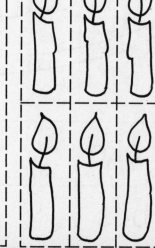

Name _____

# Hh   Hat   hat

# Name _____

Have students circle the objects that begin with the same sound as the objects at the top of the page.

# H h

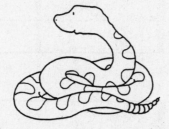

# Name _____

Direct students as they:
1. Color the picture.
2. Cut out along the dotted lines to create a puzzle.

# Puzzle Picture

Name _____

Have students color the pictures, cut them out along the dotted lines, and paste them into their pictionaries in the correct location.

_____
Name

# can read these words:

cake            candy           cup

hat             ice cream       present

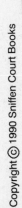

_____
Teacher                                    Date

## Teacher Notes

**Unit Word List:**                    **Unit Letter:** *Z z*

balloon    lion
monkey    snake
zebra      zoo

### Page 249  Building Prior Knowledge

Use the theme picture to develop concepts related to the zoo. The following questions can be used to stimulate language development:

Where are the people in this picture?

Have you ever been to a zoo?

What animals did you see?

What animals are in the zoo in this picture?

What are some of your favorite zoo animals?

If students are learning letter-sound relationships, have them pick out all the items in the illustration that start the same as *zoo*: zebra, zipper.

### Answers for Activity Pages

**Page 250**  Students should cut out the words at the bottom of the page and paste them in the box with the matching picture.

**Page 251**  Students should trace the first letter in each word and draw a circle around the matching picture.

**Page 252**  Students should paste the zebra, snake, lion, and monkey around *Zoo Animals.*

### Page 253  Zebra Stripes

Additional materials: construction paper cut in 1/2 inch strips

Detail of assembly:

Fold paper in half perpendicular to dotted lines and then cut across fold along dotted lines to make slits.

**Page 254**  Students should trace the first letter in the words at the top of the page, color the picture, and then trace the capital and lower-case *Zz*'s on the lines.

**Page 255**  Students should draw a line from *Zz*'s to the zebra, zipper, and zoo.

### Page 256  Roaring Lion

Additional materials: one paper bag per student

Detail of assembly:

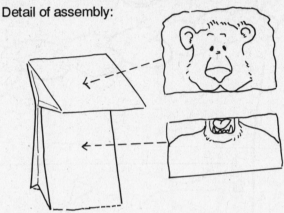

1. Color the lion and cut out along the dotted lines.
2. Paste head to the bottom of the paper bag folded flat.
3. Paste body on one side of the paper bag so that the lion's mouth tucks under the lower portion of its head.
4. Use as a hand puppet, moving hand inside bag to open and shut the lion's mouth.

## Additional Unit Activities

### Books

The following books related to the zoo might be read to the students during the completion of this unit:

*Be Nice to Spiders* by Margaret Bloy Graham, New York: Harper & Row, 1967

*Put Me in the Zoo* by Robert Lopshire, New York: Random House, 1960

*A Zoo for Mister Muster* by Arnold Lobel, New York: Harper & Row, 1962

*The White Horse* by Edith T. Hurd, New York: Harper & Row, 1970

# Name _____

After discussing the picture, have
students color: the balloons red; the
lions yellow; the monkey brown; the
snake green, the zebras black and
white.  Then have them put an *X* on
the sign that says "Zoo."

# At the Zoo

# Name _____

| balloon | lion | monkey |
|---------|------|--------|
| snake | zebra | zoo |

Have students cut out the words at the bottom of the page and paste them below the correct pictures.

| zebra | monkey | lion |
|-------|--------|------|
| snake | zoo | balloon |

# Name _____

Have students trace the first letter of the word in each box and circle the picture that matches the word.

 lion

 zoo

 zebra

 monkey

 snake

 balloon

# Name _____

Have students cut out the boxes at the bottom of the page and paste those that name zoo animals in the spaces.

Zoo Animals

zebra

snake

clown

lion

doll

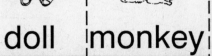
monkey

Name _____

# Zebra Stripes

Name _____

Have students trace the beginning letter in the words at the top of the page; color the picture; then trace the letters in the rows below.

Z   Zebra

z   zebra

Z Z Z Z Z Z

Z Z Z Z Z Z

Name _____

Have students draw a line from the letter in the center of the circle to each object whose name begins with that letter.

Zz

Name _____

Help students to create a paper bag puppet. See illustrated directions in the Unit 23 Teacher Notes, page 248.

# Roaring Lion

Name _____

Have students color the pictures, cut them out along the dotted lines, and paste them into their pictionaries in the correct location.

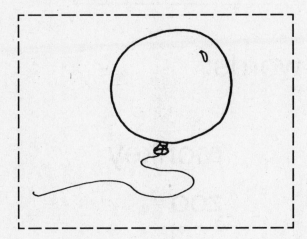

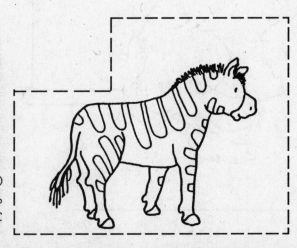

# can read these words:

| | | |
|---|---|---|
| balloon | lion | monkey |
| snake | zebra | zoo |

## Teacher Notes

**Unit Word List:**

book     chair
clock     flag
rug     table

**Unit Letter:** *R r*

### Page 260 Building Prior Knowledge

Use the theme picture to develop concepts related to the library. The following questions can be used to stimulate language development:

> Where are the children in this picture?
>
> What are they doing?
>
> Do you ever go to the library?
>
> What do you do there?
>
> Do you have a library card of your own?
>
> What can you do if you have a library card?
>
> What are some of your favorite library books?

If students are learning letter-sound relationships, have them pick out all the items in the illustration that start the same as *rug*: rabbit, rainbow, robot, rain, raccoon.

### Answers for Activity Pages

**Page 261** Students should cut out the pictures at the bottom of the page and paste them in the box with the matching words.

**Page 262** Students should trace the first letter in each word and draw a line to the matching picture.

**Page 263** Students should paste *rug, chair, flag, book, clock, table* on the books.

### Page 264 Make a Flag

Students can create their own personal flag, a family flag, or a class flag. Discuss what might be found on such a flag (favorite colors, interests).

**Page 265** Students should trace the first letter in the words at the top of the page, color the picture, and then trace the capital and lower-case *Rr*'s on the lines.

**Page 266** Students should draw a circle around rabbit, rake, rainbow, radio.

### Page 267 Clock Work

Additional materials: paper fasteners
Duplication of this page onto construction or other sturdy paper is recommended.

Detail of assembly:

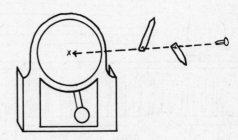

## Additional Unit Activities

### Books

The following books related to the library might be read to the students during the completion of this unit:

*Rosa-Too-Little* by Sue Felt, New York: Doubleday, 1950

*City Fun* by Marguerite Hillert, Chicago: Follett, 1981

*1 2 3 for the Library* by Mary E. Little, New York: Atheneum, 1974

### Poem

#### Clocks and Watches

Our great
Steeple clock
Goes TICK-TOCK,
TICK-TOCK;

Our small
Mantle clock
Goes TICK-TACK, TICK-TACK,
TICK-TACK, TICK-TACK;

Our little
Pocket watch
Goes Tick-a-tacker, Tick-a-tacker,
Tick-a-tacker, tack.

*Unknown*

Name _____

# At the Library

After discussing the picture, have students color: the book on the table red; the table blue; the chair yellow. Then have them circle the clock, draw a line under the flag, and put an X on the rug.

# Name _____

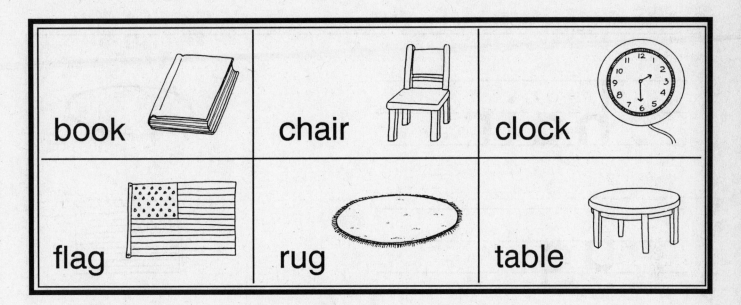

book

chair

clock

flag

rug

table

Have students cut out the pictures below and paste them above the correct words.

| | | |
|---|---|---|
| clock | flag | chair |
| book | table | rug |

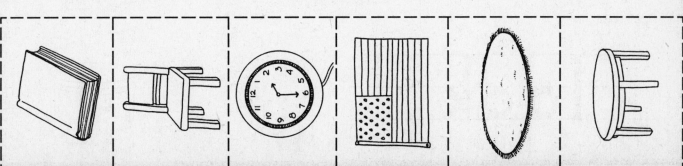

# Name _____

Have students trace the first letter of the words and draw a line from each word to the matching picture.

chair

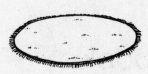

rug

flag

table

book

clock

Name _____

Have students cut out the words at the bottom of the page and paste on the books those that name things found in the library.

| rug | chair | barn | flag |
|------|-------|------|-------|
| book | clock | tub | table |

Name _____

Direct students as they color and
paste shapes and pictures in the box
below to create a flag.

# Make a Flag

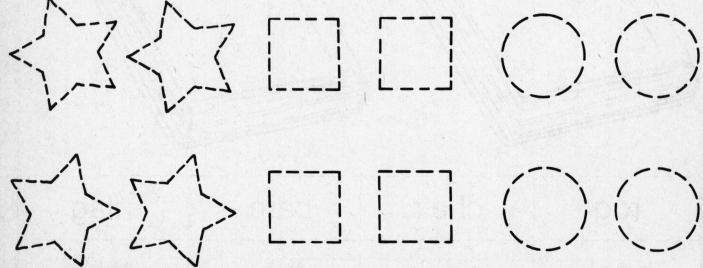

Name _____

Have students trace the beginning letter in the words at the top of the page; color the picture; then trace the letters in the rows below.

R r   Rug   rug

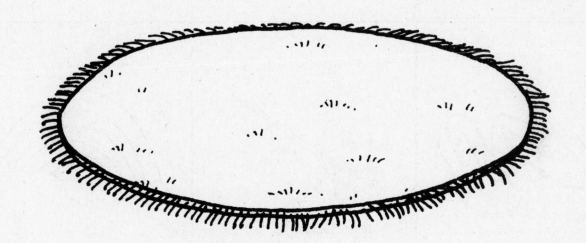

R R R R R R

r r r r r r

# Name _____

Have students circle each picture whose name begins the same as the picture in the first box.

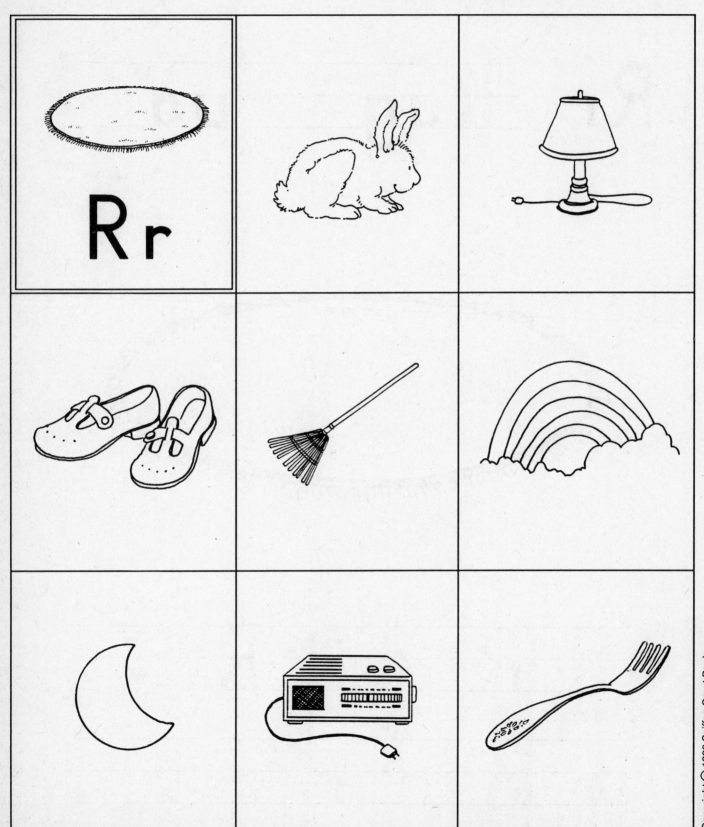

Name _____

# Clock Work

Direct students as they:
1. Color the clock and hands and cut out along the dotted lines.
2. Push a paper fastener through the X on each of the hands and then through the X on the clock.
3. Fold the tabs back to stand the clock erect.

fold

fold

Name _____

Have students color the pictures, cut them out along the dotted lines, and paste them into their pictionaries in the correct location.

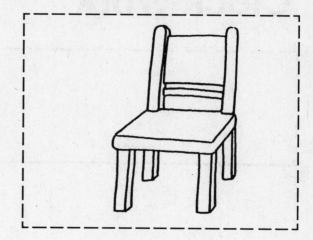

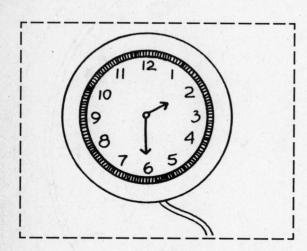

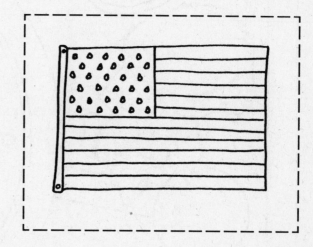

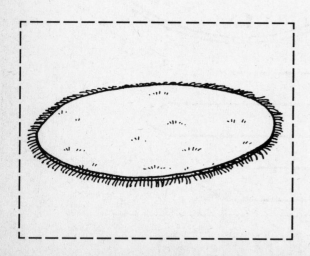

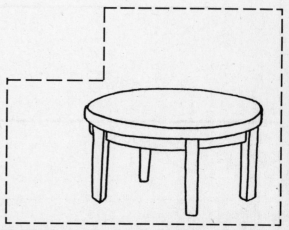

_____
Name

# can read these words:

| book | chair | clock |
| flag | rug | table |

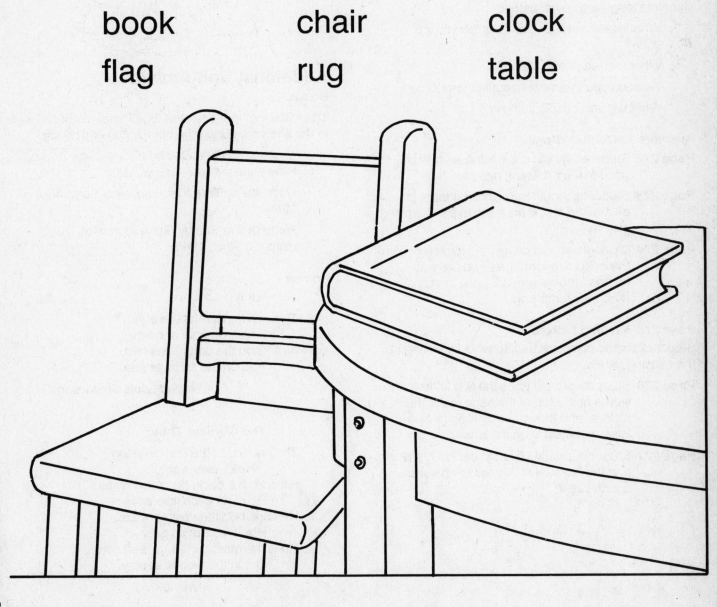

_____
**Teacher**                                                      Date

## Teacher Notes

**Unit Word List:**          **Unit Letter:** *U u*

| | |
|---|---|
| boat | frog |
| pool | squirrel |
| sun | umbrella |

### Page 271  Building Prior Knowledge

Use the theme picture to develop concepts related to summer. The following questions can be used to stimulate language development:

> What season of the year does this picture show?
>
> What are the people doing?
>
> What do you like most about summer?
>
> What will you do this summer?

### Answers for Activity Pages

**Page 272** Students should draw a line from each word to the matching picture.

**Page 273** Students should trace the first letter in each word and draw a line to the matching picture.

**Page 274** Students should paste the pictures from the bottom to form matching pairs as follows: moon-sun; tub-pool; boots-umbrella; turtle-frog.

### Page 275  Missing Letters

Students should complete the alphabet by writing in the missing letters.

**Page 276** Students should trace the first letter in the words at the top of the page, color the picture, and then trace the capital and lower-case *Uu*'s on the lines.

**Page 277** Students should color the capital *U*'s blue and the lower-case *u*'s red to reveal a beach scene.

### Page 278  Who's There?

Students should connect the dots as indicated below:

## Additional Unit Activities

### Books

The following books related to summer might be read to the students during the completion of this unit:

*Emilio's Summer Day* by Miriam Anne Bourne, New York: Harper & Row, 1966

*Umbrella* by Taro Yashima, New York: Viking, 1958

*Harry by the Sea* by Gene Zion, New York: Harper & Row, 1965

### Poems

#### Rain

The rain is raining all around,
  It falls on field and tree,
It rains on the umbrellas here,
  And on the ships at sea.

*Robert Louis Stevenson*

#### The Curliest Thing

The squirrel is the curliest thing
  I think I ever saw;
He curls his back, he curls his tail,
  He curls each little paw,
He curls his little vest so white,
  His little coat so grey--
He is the most curled-up wee soul
  Out in the woods at play!

*Unknown*

Name _____

After discussing the picture, have students color: the boat red; the frog green; the pool blue; the squirrel brown; the sun yellow; the umbrella orange.

# Summer

# Name _____

In the boxes below, have students draw a line from each word to the correct picture.

Name _____

Have students trace the first letter of the words and then draw a line from each word to the matching picture.

pool

umbrella

sun

frog

boat

squirrel

Name _____

Have students cut out the boxes at the bottom of the page and paste each beside something it goes with. Have students explain their choices.

moon

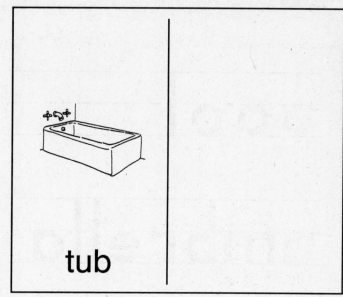

tub

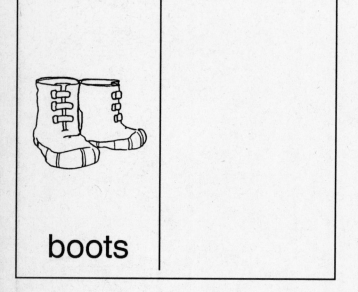

boots

turtle

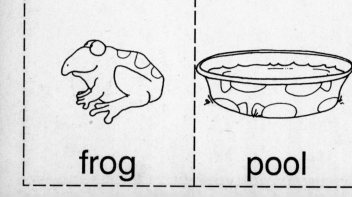

frog

pool

sun

umbrella

Direct students as they fill in the
missing letters in the alphabet below.

# Missing Letters

A __ C D __ F

H I J __ L __ N

__ P __ R S __ U

V W __ Y __

a b __ d e __ g

h __ j k __ m n

o __ q __ s t __

v __ x __ z

Name ______________________________

Have students trace the beginning letter in the words at the top of the page; color the picture; then trace the letters in the rows below.

U Umbrella

u umbrella

U U U U U U

u u u u u u

# Name _____

Have students color all the sections of the picture with capital *U*'s blue and with lower-case *u*'s red.

Name _____

Direct students as they complete the picture by connecting the dots in alphabetical order.

# Who's There?

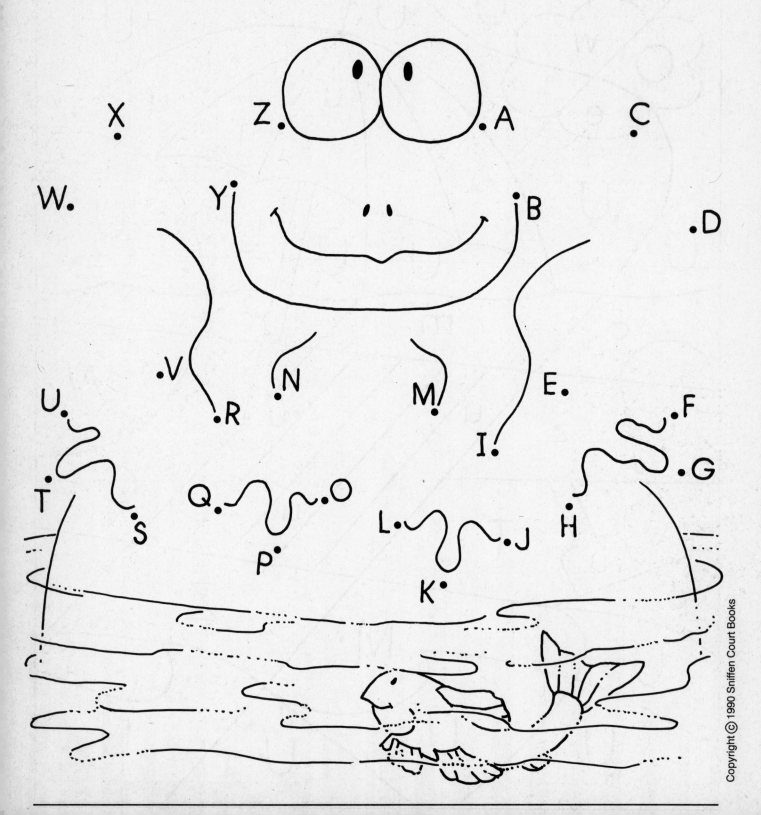

# Name _____

Have students color the pictures, cut them out along the dotted lines, and paste them into their pictionaries in the correct location.

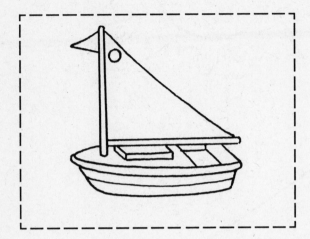

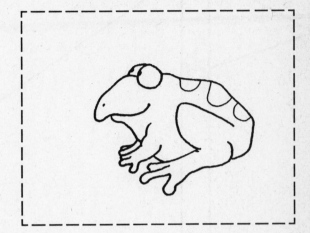

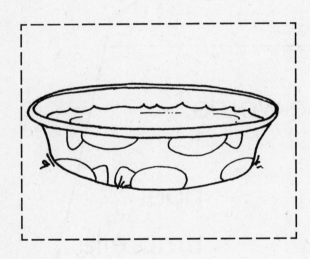

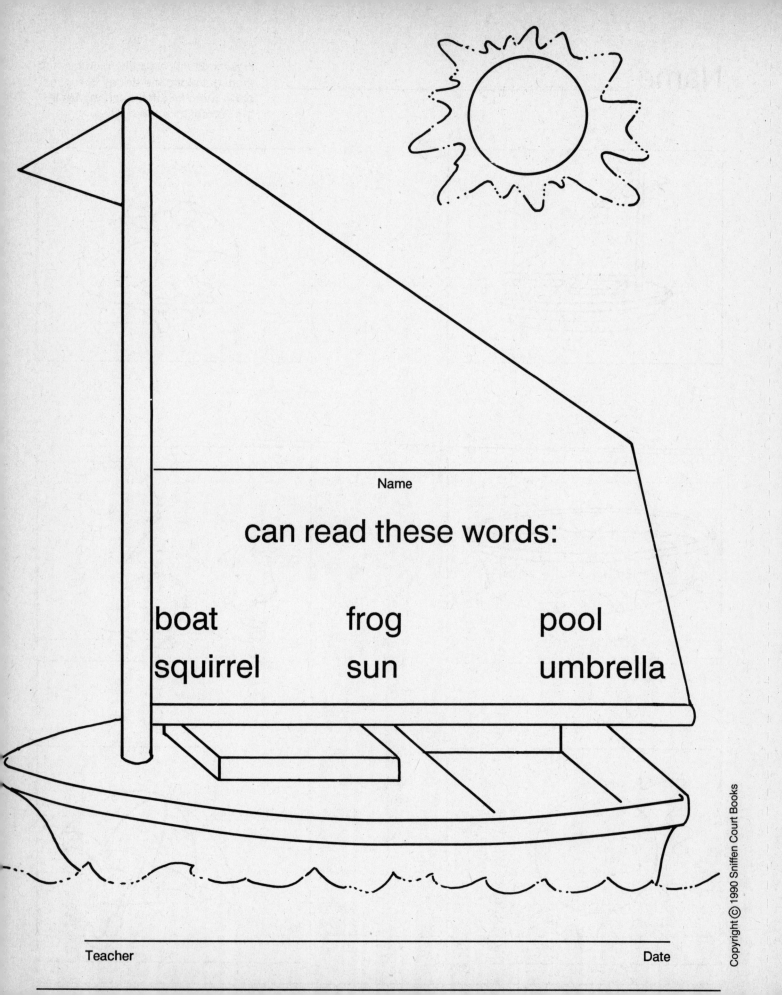

Name

can read these words:

boat          frog          pool

squirrel      sun           umbrella

Teacher                                              Date

# Name _____

Have students trace the letters. Then have them cut out the letters and paste each beside the picture whose name begins with that letter.

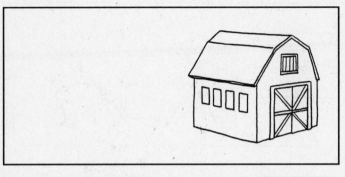

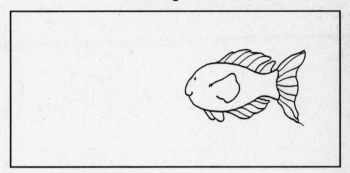

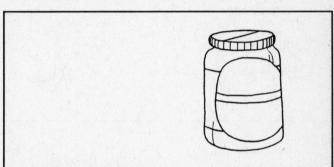

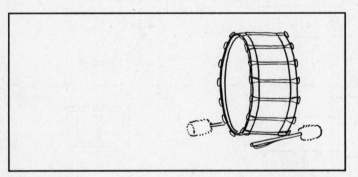

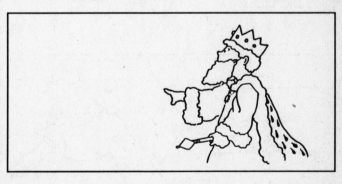

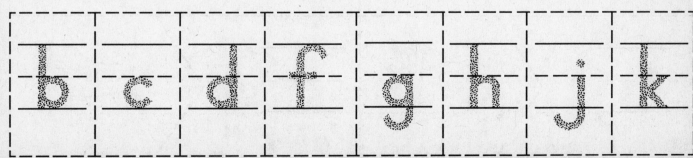

b  c  d  f  g  h  j  k

# Name _____

Have students trace each letter, cut out the puzzle, mix up the pieces, and try to match them again.

# Name _____

Have students trace the letters. Then have them cut out the shoes and paste them on the feet, matching capital and lower case letters.

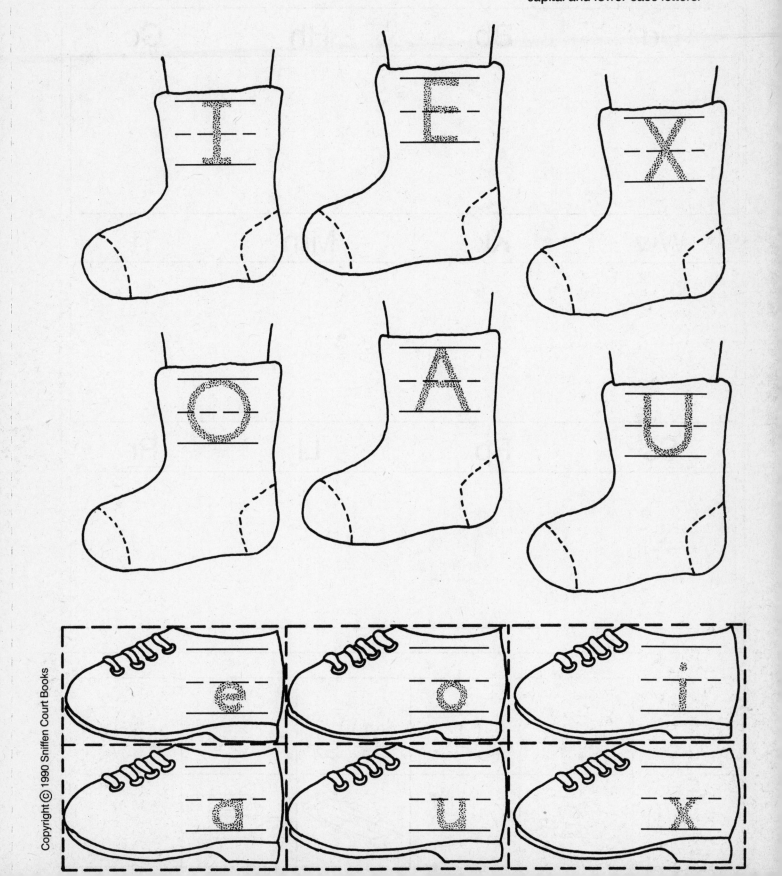

# Name _____

Have students cut out the toy pictures below and paste them on the shelves below the correct letter.

| Dd | Bb | Hh | Cc |
|----|----|----|----|

| Ww | Kk | Mm | Tt |
|----|----|----|----|

| Ss | Pp | Ll | Rr |
|----|----|----|----|

# Name _____

| | | |
|---|---|---|
| f | t | g |
| n | j | b |
| w | s | r |

Color and cut out the pictures at the bottom of the page along the dotted lines.

To play the game:

1. Each student places all the pictures in a pile face down.
2. Students take turns choosing a picture from their piles. If the beginning sound of the word pictured matches one of the letters on the game board, it should be placed over that letter.
3. The first student to complete a horizontal, vertical or diagonal row wins. For a longer game, play till the entire board is filled.

# To the Teacher

One of the major features of *Make Your Own Pictionary* is the do-it-yourself Pictionary. As the students complete each unit of *Make Your Own Pictionary*, they will have pictures of the six new words taught in that unit to add to their pictionaries. At the end of the school year, they will have a completed book to take home.

### Pictionary, Pages 1-32

These pages feature spaces for all 150 words taught, as well as empty spaces for students to add their own new words. Arranged alphabetically, the first word for each letter is identified by large letters in the upper left corner. These pages may be duplicated sequentially onto both sides of the paper if you wish to make the pictionaries of a more manageable and economic length.

The Pictionary Blank following page 32 may be duplicated onto the back of the regular pages to provide space for additional words the students might want to add to their pictionaries.

## Pictionary Assembly

Duplicate the pictionary cover page and pages 1-32 for each child. There are a number of methods and materials that will enhance the appearance and durability of the student's book.

### Front Cover

Students should color the pictionary cover and add a picture of themselves in the frame.

For added durability, copy the front cover onto construction or other sturdy paper.

The addition of a back cover of sturdy paper or lightweight cardboard is also recommended.

### Binding

All the pages should be secured together along one edge by one of the following methods:

Staple the pages together.

Punch holes along one edge and use paper fasteners or yarn to bind pages together.

Staple or fasten the entire book inside a standard file folder.

Punch holes along one edge and add the Pictionary to any standard three-ring binder.

### Storage

Set aside a special shelf in the classroom for Pictionary Storage if individual desk space is not available. Add a cheerful label to the shelf and have students take turns distributing the books when they will be in use.

Use a corrugated cardboard box as a Pictionary Center. Cut the box at an angle as shown to create bookends and decorate the box with words and drawings produced by the students.

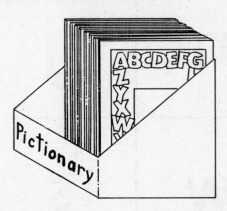

Students can make their own Pictionary Storage Pocket. Each student will need a cereal box large enough to hold the Pictionary. Have students decorate their boxes with words and pictures they have learned. Remove the box top and punch holes in one side of the box as shown. String yarn through the holes and lace the box to the back of the student's chair. Pictionaries will be in easy reach for classroom use.

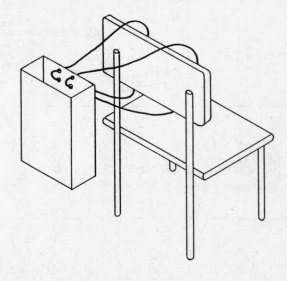

# ABCDEFG

## My Own Pictionary

_____

Name

# Aa

airplane

ant

apple

apron

_____

- - - - - - - - - - - - - - - -

_____

_____

- - - - - - - - - - - - - - - -

_____

1

# Bb

baby

ball

balloon

banana

barn

basket

| | |
|---|---|
| bat | bear |
| bed | bicycle |
| bird | blanket |

| blue | boat |
|:---:|:---:|
| book | boots |
| bottle | bowl |

4

| boy | broom |
|---|---|
| brother | brush |
| bus | butterfly |

5

# Cc

cake

candy

car

carrot

cat

chair

| | |
|---|---|
| chicken | clock |
| clown | coat |
| comb | cookies |

3

corn

cow

crayon

cup

_____

- - - - - - - - - -

_____

_____

- - - - - - - - - -

_____

8

# Dd

daddy

desk

doctor

dog

doll

door

dress

drum

duck

_____

- - - - - - - - - - - - -

_____

_____

- - - - - - - - - - - - -

_____

_____

- - - - - - - - - - - - -

_____

19

**Ee**

elephant

**Ff**

fish

five

flag

flower

fork

four

frog

_____

- - - - - - - - - - - -

_____

_____

- - - - - - - - - -

_____

_____

- - - - - - - - - - - -

_____

12

# Gg

girl

goat

green

_____
_ _ _ _ _ _ _ _ _ _
_____

_____
_ _ _ _ _ _ _ _ _ _
_____

_____
_ _ _ _ _ _ _ _ _ _
_____

13

# Hh

hat

heart

horn

horse

house

_____

- - - - - - - - - - - - - - -

_____

# Ii

ice

ice cream

# Jj

jacket

jar

_____

_ _ _ _ _ _ _ _ _ _ _ _ _

_____

_____

_ _ _ _ _ _ _ _ _ _ _ _ _

_____

# Kk

king

kite

kitten

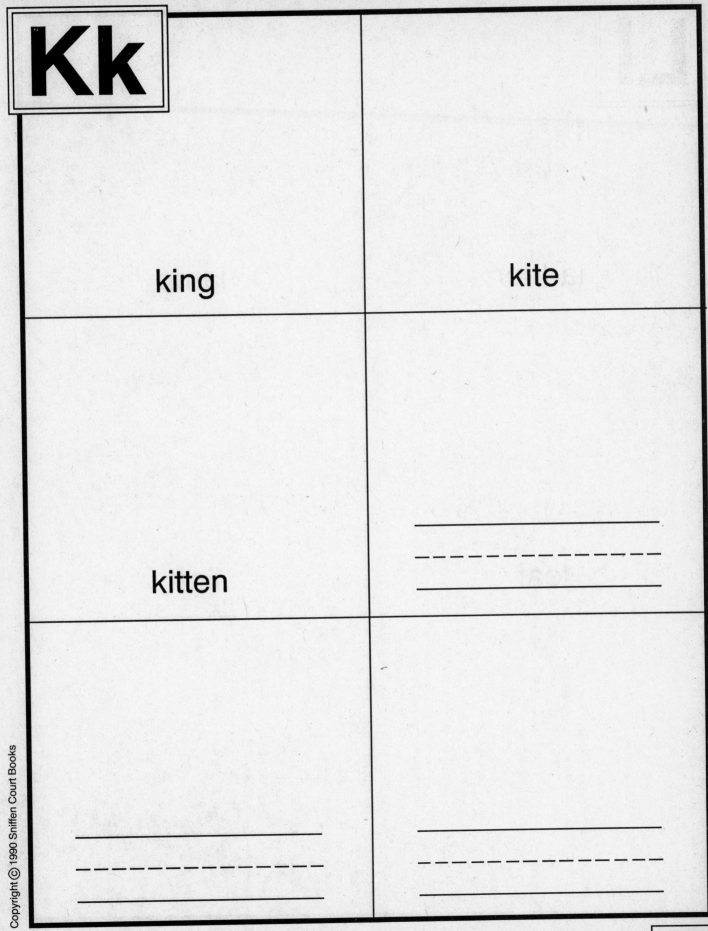

# Ll

ladder

lamp

leaf

lion

_____

- - - - - - - - - - - - - -

_____

_____

- - - - - - - - - - - - - -

_____

# Mm

milk

mitten

mommy

monkey

moon

# Nn

nest

numbers

nurse

_____
- - - - - - - - - - - - - - -
_____

# Oo

one

orange

19

# Pp

pan

pants

paper

paste

pie

pig

| | |
|---|---|
| pillow | pool |
| present | pumpkin |
| puppy | purple |

# Qq

queen

# Rr

rabbit

radio

| rainbow | rake |
| --- | --- |
| red | rug |
| _____ <br> - - - - - - - - - - - - - - <br> _____ | _____ <br> - - - - - - - - - - - - - - <br> _____ |

23

# Ss

| | |
|---|---|
| school | scissors |
| seesaw | shoes |
| sister | sled |

| | |
|---|---|
| slide | snake |
| snowman | soap |
| socks | spider |

spoon

squirrel

sun

sweater

swing

_____

- - - - - - - - - - - - -

_____

# Tt

| | |
|---|---|
| table | teacher |
| telephone | television |
| three | tiger |

| towel | train |
|-------|-------|
| tree | truck |
| T-shirt | tub |

turkey

turtle

two

_____

- - - - - - - - - - - - - -

_____

_____

- - - - - - - - - - - - - -

_____

_____

- - - - - - - - - - - - - -

_____

**U u**

umbrella

**V v**

valentine

30

# Ww

wagon

window

witch

_____
- - - - - - - - - - - - - -
_____

# Xx

x-ray

_____
- - - - - - - - - - - - - -
_____

# Yy

yellow

# Zz

zebra

zoo